CHALKED OFF!

– the School Diaries
of Morris Simpson, M.A.

Some of the characters in this book are fictitious . . .

John Mitchell taught English in Paisley for five years and is now an area manager (educational publishing) for Hodder and Stoughton. He also contributes regular articles to the *Times Scottish Education Supplement*, most particularly *Morris Simpson's School Diary*, upon which this book is based.

CHALKED OFF!

**– the School Diaries of
Morris Simpson, M.A.**

JOHN MITCHELL

Foreword by Jack McLean

Drawings by Weef

Hodder & Stoughton

Published in association with
TIMES SCOTTISH EDUCATION SUPPLEMENT

British Library Cataloguing in Publication Data

Mitchell, John
  Chalked off!
  I. Title
  823.914[F]

  ISBN 0-340-54363-9

First published 1990
Third impression 1991

Photoset by Rowland Phototypesetting Ltd
Bury St Edmunds, Suffolk.

Printed and bound in Great Britain for Hodder and Stoughton
Educational, a division of Hodder and Stoughton Ltd, Mill Road,
Dunton Green, Sevenoaks, Kent by Athenaeum Press Ltd,
Newcastle upon Tyne.

Foreword

When last we bade farewell to the hapless Morris Simpson I was still in teaching and he was getting out of it. Four years on we find Morris back into the fray and it is myself who smiles broadly in the wide expanse of Civvy Street. In the first few weeks following my release from the classroom I had nightmares that I was back in one. The month after that was worse: I dreamed I had VOLUNTEERED to go back. Eventually the incubus of my last few years in teaching receded, however. Until I came across the fresh adventures of Morris Simpson in the world of education . . .

Dear God, Morris is back. This prig, this prating, prattling, sometimes prudish PRAT is back among the dominies; a little wiser, it is true, but not much – as this chronicle by Simpson's amanuensis, Mr John Mitchell, will show. Mr Mitchell allows you to glimpse more than Simpson's progress – he draws the curtain back and lets you see the ghastly nightmare of the modern school. My bad dreams were only dreams after all; they are reality for the teachers.

Reality now. John Mitchell even acknowledges reality in a warning to you all. 'Some of the characters in this book are fictitious . . .' he says. No they're not. I recognised every one of them. Every school staffroom contains horribly accurate versions of them. The cynics and the burned-out and the obviously insane. The beastly enthusiasts and the chaps who would lick out the toilets for an extra fiver. The barking-mad Trotskyists ever ready to defend Tariq Ali or Jimmy Boyle but determined to get Maggie, Maggie, Maggie, Out, Out, Out. The teachers on the far Right who would have an education only for those who lived in bought houses in leafy suburbs. Oh it is rare fun in the teaching game. You could go on.

Morris Simpson has gone on. When last we met him he was more than glad to find himself another profession in which to act like the dafty he is. Now he has returned to find himself with a few more spondulicks in his back tail and the ruinous strike a matter of memory. But things have changed and not for the better. Read through this book and find out how. Why is another question. If the teachers of a few years back essentially took an unlikely anger into strike action because they could stand no more senseless innovation, then their strike failed miserably. Find out all about multi-cultural education and TVEI and SCOTVEC and Lord knows how many more acronyms: the full panoply of modern educational gimcrackery. Discover the casuistry of the education officials: sophistry which would do credit to the wiliest Jesuit. Uncover what is actually happening to your children in the schools.

In this sorry saga even Morris starts to think again, as well he might. I am not sure I am doing the right thing in contributing the foreword to this marvellous exposé. If I tell you that every parent, every teacher, every education official, and every politician must read this samizdat from the chalk-face; well, you have to buy it first to find that out. This book is even funnier than the first one. This book is even more tear-inducing. This book is worth a thousand educational reports. This book shows you how it is. And glad I am that I am out of the entire tragi-comedy for ever, and in another, greener, field.

Jack McLean
Education Correspondent, *The Glasgow Herald*

Prologue

WEEF

'*To enter the teaching profession once may be regarded as a misfortune; to enter it a second time borders on sheer bloody carelessness . . .*'

David Pickup, assistant principal religious education/assistant geography teacher, Parkland High School.

Those readers of *The Times Scottish Education Supplement* who followed the first two probationary years of Morris Simpson, Scotland's rawest teaching recruit, were distressed – but sympathetic – when

Simpson chose to hang up his duster at the end of that second year. His baptism into the world of education had coincided with one of the country's largest ever teacher disputes, and Morris eventually chose to leave without even attaining the benefit of his 'parchment' – the prize of full certification with the General Teaching Council, normally awarded to teachers who stagger through to the end of a second probationary year.

His headteacher's refusal to grant such a parchment, and Simpson's subsequent decision to leave the profession, were adequately chronicled in his first volume of educational memoirs (*Class Struggle: A Probationer's Diary*), after which departure Morris Simpson chose to enter the world of pre-school education as the leader of a locally based creative play team.

Alas, his new job did not provide the fulfilment which a man of his dedication might reasonably expect. A succession of untoward incidents, coupled with a letter from his old friend David Pickup – geography teacher, recently retrained as religious education specialist – which outlined some of the recent salary benefits accorded to teachers, led Morris to think long and hard about his future career plans.

In June, just at the end of a long and weary session, David Pickup received a letter. It was from Morris Simpson, and is reprinted below . . .

Dear Pickup,

Many thanks for your letter last week, which kept me in touch with recent events at Parkland High. As you know, it's a year now since I left, and I can only apologise for not having kept in closer contact with you all. I was pleased, of course, to learn that Miss Honeypot's enforced maternity leave had concluded with happy issue last winter, though am still somewhat distressed to learn of her bitterness over the Head's refusal to provide crèche facilities for the infant; to my mind, the woman has little notion of her own responsibilities in bringing up the child, and her cavalier attitude revives unpleasant memories of our summer trip abroad with the 4th year some time ago.

Otherwise, it's good to hear that an air of normality has returned to school since the cessation of industrial hostilities last session and – given the news I'll be breaking to you in the course of this letter – even better to hear of your improved financial position since last we met.

Of course, the fact that you've been 'lifted up on high', as it were, since the successful completion of your sabbatical retraining in Religious Education will have made a tremendous difference to the monthly pay-slip, but I was more than a little intrigued to learn of the enormous salary leaps attained by some of the profession's less elevated recruits as a result of the government's generosity last Autumn.

Now you know as well as the next man, Pickup, that I certainly didn't enter – or leave – teaching because of the money, but I'd have to confess that I found myself gazing covetously on some of the extravagantly constructed salary scales for teachers, copies of which you were kind enough to send me.

To be honest, things haven't been exactly ideal since I took up this post as leader of the area's pre-school creative play team. What I *had* envisaged as a job to tap my creative will and enthusiasm for launching exciting new initiatives in the field of pre-school education has turned out to be little more than a euphemistic title for a glorified child-minder. Sadly, most of the parents take little interest in our scheme, and view the centre as a free baby-sitting service provided at the taxpayer's expense.

Worse still, you might recall the attractively decorated 'play-bus' for which I had such high hopes at the beginning of my contract? It was unfortunately subject to repeated bouts of vandalism ranging from the relatively minor, but frequent, occasions when its tyres would be let down, to the distressing attack which necessitated the arrival of a fire-fighting unit to extinguish an arson attack – initiated, I might add, by one of the children for whom the facility had been provided in the first place. Bloody kids.

Unfortunately, government funding has not been available to replace the vehicle and I learn that my peripatetic role has been reduced to one of static immobility at the local community centre, where the most exciting diversion I can muster for my charges is a session of Plasticine modelling!

In short, Pickup, it's all become too depressing for words, and I've handed in my notice. My disenchantment with secondary schools was as nothing compared to the drained exhaustion which I've experienced in the nether regions of educational provision.

With such thoughts in mind, I hope it won't come as too much of a shock for you to learn that I intend making a reappearance at Parkland High! I did, of course, make several applications for posts completely outwith the educational service, but there seem to be very few avenues of opportunity for someone with my training and experience; in the meantime, therefore, I've decided to make a determined effort to relaunch my teaching career.

Now I know that my track record in the past wasn't too impressive, and I readily acknowledge that, without the assistance of the English adviser (a close personal friend of my mother), it might have been rather tricky to find a suitable post. In point of fact, I stipulated that Parkland High was probably the *last* school in the Region where I wanted to be, but it appears that Miss Bowman's department is the only one with a vacancy: ironically enough, I understand that it's my *own* job which I'm getting back, the authorities having wheeled in four supply teachers since I left twelve months ago!

It is with mixed feelings of apprehension and prodigality, therefore, that I anticipate a return during the third week of August. I am still left, of course, with the somewhat bitter taste of rejection since the headmaster's refusal to recommend my full registration with the GTC at the end of last session; after much thought, however, I have decided that it is my firm intention to overcome the petty-minded nature of his vindictive action and fulfil my long cherished hopes of becoming a fully certified teacher . . .

To be honest, I'm rather looking forward to it all. See you in August, Pickup – and save me a coffee mug!

Professionally yours,

Morris

August

There can be few ex-teachers who – having once left the traumas of classroom life behind – ever feel impelled to rejoin a profession where a verbal assault can often be the least of their worries. It takes a special kind of man to agree that marking jotters of an evening really *can* be more entertaining than a night on the town. It takes a special kind of man to reckon that a school trip to the local zoo really *is* more interesting than two weeks on a continental holiday. And it takes a special kind of man to believe that a second year class showering him with water-bombs on April 1st is a heart-warming illustration of his personal popularity with the pupils.

Morris Simpson was such a man.

An indefatigable optimist, he consistently looked forward to going to work each day. When other teachers complained about their conditions of service, Morris Simpson told them they were lucky to get such short terms and long holidays.

When pupils talked throughout one – or all – of his carefully prepared lessons, Morris was happy to witness their freedom from the petty restrictions of authority, sensing a positive outcome in what he quaintly termed a series of 'unconstructed communication situations'.

In short – and this has to be admitted – Morris Simpson was a bit of a prat. But his heart was in the right place, and it is difficult to restrain a fond admiration for his enthusiastic anticipation of the forthcoming term.

It would take some time, of course, to familiarise himself with the plethora of educational developments to have emerged since his departure: the arrival of the Technical, Vocational and Educational Initiative (TVEI), for example, was going to mean a great deal more at Parkland High than Morris might ever have expected, and he was about to learn that the initials PAT now stood for so much more than the Professional Association of Teachers, that union to which he had once, briefly, belonged. Now, they also stood for Planned Activity Time, which was probably the major bone of contention following on from the teachers' pay settlement: in an attempt to formalise the preparation of new curriculum materials, staff now had to stay behind at school after the departure of their charges for periods of one to two hours during one night each week.

It was what many teachers had been doing for years anyway – and, it must be said, what many teachers had *never* done – but the variations in regional practice meant that a high percentage of teachers felt that their employers were more interested in getting a 'pound of flesh' than in securing proper educational provision.

Depending upon your own point of view, then, PAT was either an official recognition of the fact that teachers do a great deal of unseen work, or it was a gross breach of personal freedom which meant that your family had to have a late tea every Tuesday. At Parkland High, however, they were still trying to think of ideas to fill the time.

Such concerns, though, were far from Morris Simpson's mind as he prepared for the last Monday of his summer holiday. Of more immediate concern was the reception he was likely to receive from his former colleagues on Tuesday. He certainly hoped to make a better impresion upon Mr Ross, the headmaster, than hitherto, but he dreaded further confrontation with Mr Tod, the depute. The man had never really taken to Morris, who in turn had felt badly let down by his lack of professional support – especially during the darkest hours of those first probationary years.

It was at this point that a representative from *The Times Scottish Education Supplement* heard of Morris's return to the classroom. His suggestion that the further experiences of an everyday probationary teacher might continue to be of interest to the educational world was met with no small degree of scepticism by Simpson. However, a

6

three-course lunch and the promise of improved monetary reward for such jottings gave him pause for thought.

On the grave understanding, therefore, that financial considerations were furthest from his mind, Morris once more agreed to the regular publication of extracts from his diary. For some inexplicable reason, he felt that their appearance might help to encourage young teachers in a similar position to himself. His first week back in harness did not augur well, as this first diary extract will reveal . . .

Monday – 1st in-service day

A disastrous day. Having expected to recommence my teaching career at Parkland High tomorrow, and consequently enjoying my last lie-in of the holiday period, I was understandably dismayed to receive a late morning telephone call from Mr Tod, the depute head, demanding to know of my whereabouts during what had apparently been decreed the first in-service day of the academic year.

I endeavoured to explain that such an unfortunate misunderstanding over the starting date could hardly be considered my fault, having received no formal notification of my reappointment from the staffing department, let alone any details for the new term's opening arrangements.

Unfortunately, the man's tolerance for sympathetic understanding seems to have improved little in the twelve months since I left, and I thought it wise to respond promptly to his inelegantly couched suggestion that I make immediate arrangements to turn up by lunchtime.

As things turned out, I needn't have hurried overmuch: my arrival outside the school gates at the start of lunch hour coincided with a mass exodus of staff intent upon grasping one last holiday opportunity to take advantage of the liberal licensing laws pertaining in the local public house. Consequently, the school bore close resemblance to the *Marie Celeste*, and I found myself in the solitary company of Mr Crichton, our janitorial assistant, in the school dining hall.

'Hmmph. So yur back, then?' was his opening conversational gambit. Mindful of the man's position, I felt little inclination to mount an explanation of the motives behind my return to the teaching profession and simply offered a dignified affirmative, a dignity unfortunately shaken by Mr Crichton's subsequent observation:

'Ur odd shoes "in", this year, Mistur Simpson?'

I begged his pardon and asked for elaboration.

'Odd shoes. Ur they "*in*"? Latest fashion?'

With slow-dawning comprehension, I realised that his fixed stare was directed towards my feet, clad – as they were – in alternately coloured shoes, one brown, one black.

My stuttered explanation of a hasty departure from home was met with solicitously raised eyebrows and the merest hint of a grin which played around his lips. I thought it better to ignore the man's dumb insolence and abandoned the conversation with a muttered expression of intent to go and tidy out my classroom.

'Aye. If ye've goat wan,' Mr Crichton called after me, a riposte whose meaning was clarified by Mr Tod when I sought him out after lunch. Happily, his prandial refreshments had at least left him in a more benevolent frame of mind, and he seemed quite amenable as I put the question of my teaching facilities to him.

'Yes, Simpson, I'm afraid Mr Crichton's quite correct. Your old classroom's no longer available for teaching purposes. It's going to be used by the TVEI and we're looking –'

'The what?'

'Technical, Vocational and – um – the –'

'Yes?'

'Well, it's a government funded scheme. Very prestigious for us to get it here, y'know. So you'll have to be peripatetic for a while. Temporarily, of course.'

Mindful of my first meeting with Mr Tod, wherein a similar assurance saw me wandering the school corridors for eleven months of my first probationary year, I decided to make a stand there and then.

'No. I'm sorry, Mr Tod, but I shall have to *insist* upon a room of my own. The nature of English teaching nowadays necessitates a room which allows the teacher to accumulate a store of resource items and textual materials which are *impossible* to cart around the school on a daily basis. And what's more, with the new demands for Standard Grade, I shall simply *have* to be placed in a room with permanently installed audio-visual equipment and a –'

'Stow it, Simpson.' The approachable veneer was erased, and Mr Tod returned to form in a gratuitous and venomous attack: 'As far as your room's concerned, I'll see what I can do, but don't expect miracles. You might not realise it, son, but news of your return to this school didn't exactly fill us all with unbridled enthusiasm. Be that as it may, you're here now, and we're stuck with you. But just

8

remember one thing,' – Tod clenched his teeth –'if you start making my life as much of a misery as you did last time round, then I'll make bloody sure yours is ten times worse. Got it?'

'Yes, Mr Tod, but –'

'And another thing.'

'Yes, Mr Tod?'

'There's a staff meeting in the lecture theatre tomorrow at 9am. Be there. Be on time. And *get your bloody shoes changed*!'

Head bowed, I shuffled towards the English store cupboard. I wonder what my timetable will be like?

Tuesday – 2nd in-service day

Mr Tod's criticism of my personal appearance took on ironic bent when I noted the sartorial inelegance of my teaching collleagues at this morning's staff meeting. Unconcerned to mount any attempt at professional appearance, over half of them had turned up in casual clothing, a state of affairs which they apparently justify by the fact that, as no teaching is to be performed during in-service days, they can wear what they damned well like! A disgraceful attitude, but I reserved such thoughts to myself as I sidled into the back row of the lecture theatre and ensconced myself next to our new assistant principal teacher of religious education, Mr Pickup, improbably attired in denim jeans, baseball boots and an impossibly gaudy T Shirt.

'Ah! The Prodigal Son returns! Welcome back, Simpson – ready for the fray, old man?'

'Just about, Pickup,' I replied. 'And congrats on the promotion.'

Pickup's snorted rejoinder, wherein he explained that, despite being in charge of RE, he was still expected to remain as point six of a Geography teacher, with all of the consequent timetabling difficulties that such a position entailed, reminded me of my severe reservations concerning the timetable given to me my Miss Bowman yesterday afternoon. I told Pickup that it seemed to comprise, in the main, four sets of first and second year classes for half of their respective English teaching, the only bright spot being a sixth year group, whose demands should at least give me some kind of intellectual challenge. He reckoned my plans to start off their SYS course with an in-depth study of TS Eliot should prove a welcome respite from the non-certificate work with the junior school.

Our conversation was interrupted by the headmaster gathering our attention for a meeting whose first thirty minutes seemed exclusively concerned with his continuing enthusiasm for handing out information sheets and then reading through them, one line at a time. Sadly, his most pressing and urgent educational requirement was that the staff should desist *immediately* from leaving the tea-urn switched on throughout the entire teaching day, a request occasioned by the enormous cost to the region of replacing burnt-out elements, and a request which – to the best of my recollection – was made at my very first such meeting three long years ago. *Plus ca change* . . .

My morning depression was heightened further by Miss Bowman's afternoon revelation that my sixth year class, far from being the academic élite, is a motley collection of O grade second repeats for whom TS Eliot is unlikely to prove a major attraction. As if this were not enough, Mr Tod approached me in the car park at 4 o'clock.

'By the way, Simpson,' he smiled curtly, 'I've managed to get you a room of your own after all . . .'

My protestations of gratitude were guillotined by his explanation of its location: 'No. That's all right. You're sharing a hut with Pickup. He's got A56 and you're next door in A57.'

'A hut? But Mr Tod –'

Indifferent to my querulous plea, Tod turned on his heel and departed, leaving me to ponder my banishment to the mobile classroom in the school playground, and all its attendant inconvenience: insecure storage facilities, nomadic pupils arriving twenty minutes late for lessons, inadequate communication with the rest of my department, no toilet facilities for eight hundred yards, noise-laden hollow floors – all of these and, worst burden of all, a flat roof! I dread the winter months . . .

Teaching Begins

Wednesday

The first teaching day of my restarted career, a day marked by confusion and acrimonious discussion which served to further concern over the wisdom of my return to the profession. The morning was largely spent in a 25–minute wait outside my new classroom, accompanied by a 30–strong second year class; since Mr Tod has seen fit to reallocate my classroom as a TVEI Base, the beginning of my banishment to the huts was marked by the absence of any suitable key with which to open the glorified telephone box I am to share with Mr Pickup – who, it eventually turned out, was holding the damned thing for safe keeping.

My disposition was not improved by the headmaster's decision to order an early closure for pupils this afternoon, in order to formalise his plans for future in-service days this year – as if we hadn't all had enough of them after the last two days! To be honest, I was appalled at the gross waste of time occasioned by the entire farrago.

It seems hard to believe, but we actually spent ninety minutes trying deperately to think of discussion topics which would pad out the more reflective moments of our additional contracted duties. To explain, the headmaster has been directed to prepare a timetable of in-service days by the divisional education officer, as outlined in the new conditions of service; in return for 'thirty pieces of silver', as my departmental colleague Mr Pringle puts it, we are to report for five extra days of in-service provision. The only trouble seems to be that nobody quite knows how to fill them! It was all too much for Pringle . . .

'Just a minute, headmaster,' he called out after Mr Major had proposed a session on interactive video for third-year guidance staff: 'Let me get this straight. What's the precise purpose of this meeting?'

'To decide what we're going to discuss at in-service, Pringle,' snapped a somewhat tetchy reply.

'I see. So – correct me if I'm wrong – we're having a meeting to discuss what we're going to discuss at the next meeting.'

'That's right.'

Unable to control the derisive guffaw which rose to his throat, Pringle hastily withdrew a handkerchief from his breast pocket and stifled his laughter. He seemed to take little interest in the rest of the discussion, and fell to completing his newspaper crossword, muttering comments the while about a 'brave new world'.

I suppose his impending retirement has left him disinterested in advancing the frontiers of educational philosophy.

Thursday

Another long search for my hut's key, this time in the company of my sixth year O grade second repeat class. Its unavailability took at least twenty minutes off our first double period together, a fact which caused me less distress the longer our eventual lesson continued.

The entire class seems unfortunately composed of underachieving school phobics and socially repellent adolescents; the major source of concern is a massively-framed girl called Rose McShane: aside from hurling abusive insults at the sound of every name I read out on the class register, the girl has a disgusting habit of eating toffee-filled chocolate bars and spitting the half-chewed contents from her mouth on to whichever wall happens to be nearest her desk. I tried relocating her seat in the middle of the room, but she has an impressive firing range . . .

Popped next door to ask Mr Pickup for some information on the girl, and was horrified to learn that she's been in five previous schools since third year.

'So we're her sixth educational establishment in three years?'

Pickup nodded grim confirmation.

'But what on earth's *wrong* with the girl? She seems to be completely uncontrollable –'

'That's also right.' Pickup seemed about to laugh, but continued in serious vein: 'Usual story, I'm afraid – it's the parents' fault, not hers. The child comes from the most appalling background; given the kind of social framework she inhabits outwith school, it's lucky she's no worse than she is.'

Horrified at such a revelation, I enquired about the possibility of inviting her parents to speak to me. Pickup seemed momentarily amused, then straightened his face and suggested I was welcome to try. I wonder what he finds so funny about it all?

Friday

A difficult morning for introductions. I met three of my four first year classes, one after the other: trying to fit ninety names to faces in the space of three hours can be somewhat confusing.

Most of my spare time, however, was taken up with the perplexing issue of Rose McShane, and the alarming realisation that Pickup's been having a joke at my expense.

To explain, I couldn't help but notice the girl being dropped at the school gates this morning from the back door of a brand new BMW, and sought out Mr Major at lunchtime. He was greatly amused to hear that I considered the child a victim of social deprivation.

'Good God, Simpson: who on earth told you that?'

'Mr Pickup, yesterday afternoon. He told me the girl's behaviour all stemmed from her home background.'

'Did he now?' Major chortled. 'Well, in a sense, the old bugger's probably right.'

'How d'you mean?'

'Um. Look, Simpson,' Major seemed hesitant: 'Tell it not abroad, but our darling Rose is the daughter of some fairly important parents, and it'd probably be wise to keep a low profile on this one.'

'Low profile?'

'Yes. Her mother's in charge of the area social work department, and her dad's chief educational psychologist for the entire ruddy division. They don't want –'

I interrupted. 'Hang on, Major. You don't mean to tell me that Rose McShane – *the* Rose McShane – is the child of . . .'

'The very same,' he confirmed. 'Fruit of his loins, and all that. Savage, really, isn't it? The parents get paid telephone numbers for sorting out the problems of the lower orders, and all the while they've got a vicious little bitch of their own, running riot at home and causing untold misery for every teacher who's ever had the misfortune to cross her path.'

'But that's appalling! Why can't they do something about it?'

'Oh, they've tried,' sighed Major, 'they've tried. Unfortunately, their ideas on child-centred self-discipline don't seem to coincide with any school's they've ever come across. In short, Simpson, the girl's got ten more months to go, and we're landed with her. I *wouldn't* advise calling in the parents for a discussion – just stick her in a corner and try to forget about her.'

Major's solution is all very well, but seems to ignore the educational welfare of the child – not to mention the multidirectional assaults from soggy lumps of chocolate toffee. I think I *shall* call in the parents for interview. Who knows? I may even make a name for myself.

September

Morris Simpson had spent much time studying the multitudinous theories of behaviour modification, so beloved of Rose McShane's parents. He had a merit certificate in educational psychology to prove it. Never punish the child, only encourage. Respond only to good behaviour, and simply ignore bad behaviour. Remember – always – that the fault for poor classroom discipline is more likely to lie at the teacher's door than the pupil's: he or she is probably bored, and the teacher has done too little to engage the child's attention. It had all seemed simple enough at college.

And yet it just didn't seem to work with Rose McShane. No matter how solicitous, no matter how approachable he tried to be with her, the girl refused to acknowledge Morris's authority.

But Rose McShane, and pupils like her, had been problems for many teachers before Morris. In the days before the abolition of corporal punishment, any such anti-social or disruptive tendencies as Rose displayed would have been dealt swift and painful retribution in the form of a Lochgelly tawse. For better or for worse, such action would at least have the undeniable merit of restoring short-term order, no matter the longer term psychological effects on the recipient.

The alternative sanctions of punishment exercises, 'sin-bins' and, ultimately, suspensions from school, were now the only forms of disciplinary action available to beleaguered teachers. And, as will become apparent, even such procedures as these were under threat.

These first few weeks back at school, then, proved trying times for Morris: notwithstanding the problem of Rose McShane, he was rediscovering the complications which will frequently arise in a probationer's timetable, composed, as it was, of a motley collection of junior classes who came to see him for only part of their English time. At least he had a room of his own, an unusual privilege for one so young – even if it did have a flat roof.

But it was Rose McShane who caused him the greatest concern. Rude, arrogant, and potentially violent, it was time that something was done about her. Some six weeks into the term, the eventual decision to call in her parents for interview was not taken lightly, but Morris was genuinely afraid that something serious was going to happen if he did not take the matter in hand. Sadly, he failed to get very far, as his diary entry for the last week of September will testify.

Monday

A traumatic interview with the parents of Rose McShane, the large and maladjusted recruit to my O grade second repeat class. Mr McShane will not accept my reluctance to allow his daughter unfettered and limitless freedom to behave in whichever manner she chooses. In particular, he refuses to believe that the girl's unmannerly – and frequently obscene – interruptions to my carefully prepared lessons are a source of constant irritation.

'But Rose has *always* been an outspoken child, Mr Simpson. She simply requires a sympathetic ear . . .'

'Yes,' concurred his wife. 'She's actually extremely bright. The problems only begin when her attention isn't diverted into constructive channels.'

My protestations to the effect that it was difficult to engage these attentions while she persisted in the disgusting habit of spitting

16

semi-chewed lumps of toffee on to the nearest classroom wall brooked little sympathy. Furthermore, I felt constrained to inform them that their daughter seemed predisposed to the opportunity of launching violent physical attacks towards any member of the class who ventured to disagree with her opinions.

'As you'll appreciate, Mr McShane,' I tried to convince him, 'it makes group discussions somewhat fraught.'

'I'm sorry, Mr Simpson,' he returned, 'but we've always taught Rose to stand up for what she believes in. Discipline within the classroom is entirely your concern. Now, if you'll excuse us, my wife and I must be going . . .'

I think this could be an ongoing problem. My only source of present consolation is that at least I don't see the wretched girl tomorrow.

Tuesday

The difficulties associated with my timetable are becoming increasingly apparent. Its makeshift and patchwork appearance owes much to Miss Bowman's reluctance to give me complete responsibility for any one group of children – with the solitary exception of the O grade second repeats. I am left, for example, with four separate groups of first year pupils for half of their English allocation, an arrangement which leads to severe difficulties in differentiating one class from another.

The only discernible merit to such a system is the fact that I have been hitherto able to cut down on preparation time by repeating entire lesson units with each group. Unfortunately, my bluff was called this morning by Angela Swift of 1F, who quietly but pointedly refused to write an essay about 'My Favourite Things' on the grounds that she'd already *written* two such pieces:

'Really?' I asked her. 'In whose class?'

'Yours, sir,' she grimaced. 'And both times you played us the same Julie Andrews record before it –'

My embarrassment was increased by the revelation that I had apparently marked both essays without noticing their precise similarities to each other – and heightened further by the contradictory grades she had been awarded for what turned out to be the same piece of work!

I made a few congratulatory remarks on her astute observation and have promised to review the grades. Strangely enough, nobody else in the class seems to have noticed the repetition.

Wednesday

The case of Rose McShane took on dramatic proportions this morning during a group discussion on violence which I'd initiated as part of her class's theme study. In what she later claimed to be an attempt to bring reality to the conversation, the girl withdrew a fearsome looking wooden stake from the voluminous folds of her bomber jacket and advanced on Sinnot, a spotty faced youth who had stupidly seen fit to cast doubts upon her parentage in the course of our discussion.

'You say that wance mair,' she screeched, '– an' ah'll split ye – awright?'

'Try it, McShane, an' see whit ye get back!' bawled Sinnot.

The situation looked like becoming serious until Mr Pickup, with whom I share a hut, barged in to discover the nature of the disturbance; assessing the problem at a glance, he advanced on Rose and swiftly disarmed the girl, leaving her inelegantly spreadeagled on the floor as a consequence.

'Little trick I picked up in the Army,' he smiled at me. Shaking violently, I made profuse thanks and located a referral sheet from my desk.

Aside from the obvious distress which such an event has caused, I am at least consoled by the certainty that young Miss McShane is unlikely to disturb me in the coming weeks. A suspension is automatic for an offence as serious as this – and I can only hope that its duration is infinite!

Thursday

Rose McShane isn't to be suspended. The depute head called me into his office this morning and explained that a referral would suffice on this occasion.

'But Mr Tod!' I protested: 'That's impossible! The girl was two steps away from facing an assault charge, let alone anything more serious. You can't mean to tell me that –'

'Yes, I'm afraid I *do* mean to tell you,' he interrupted. 'And I'm afraid it's nothing to do with the fact that the offensive big lump nearly sidelined Sinnot for a week.'

'No?'

'No. Actually, we might all have been quite grateful if she had. The point is, Simpson, that the head's trying to avoid as many suspensions as possible this session.'

'Avoid them? But whatever for? They're practically the only disciplinary measure left to us since –'

'Aye. But not for long, methinks.'

'Not for long? How – what d'you mean, Mr Tod?'

The depute leaned conspiratorially over his desk and whispered: 'The councillors, Simpson. The councillors.'

'I'm sorry?'

'They're not happy about it. Not happy at all. Children being deprived of their right to an education, y'see. Taxpayer shelling out good money to bestow an education on the lower orders, then the bloody teachers stop them coming to school to get it.'

'But that's all wrong! And –'

'Maybe it is. But that's how they see it. Rumour has it that suspensions'll soon be going the way of the belt: completely *verboten*, you understand. In their eyes, even the most insufferably offensive child in the world's got an inalienable right to an education – and they'll make sure he gets it, even if they have to tie him to a chair and force it down his bloody throat!'

Mr Tod obviously feels strongly about the matter. I left his office in reflective mood.

Friday

A summons to the headmaster's office this afternoon in the company of Mr Pickup. My assumption that we were to be accorded joint congratulations for defusing the potential assault on Wednesday was, sadly, unfulfilled. On the contrary, Mr Ross seemed intent to place the blame for the whole wretched event upon me (for allowing such a situation to develop in the first place) and upon Pickup (for using unnecessary force in quelling the disturbance).

His audience speechless, the head continued:

'The point is, gents, that Rose McShane narrowly escaped serious injury herself after Mr Pickup's intervention. Two feet nearer a desk, and we'd have been in serious trouble.'

'Good God, headmaster!' blurted Pickup: 'You can't –'

'*If* you'll allow me to finish, Mr Pickup,' intoned Mr Ross, 'what

19

I'd like to suggest is that you both take a look at this . . .' he passed a folder over the desk. 'It's a course.'

'A course?' I queried.

'Yes. Open to all. And covering a topic that's of more than immediate interest.'

Pickup just managed to stifle a derisive snort as he scanned the title engraved on the course folder: 'Conflict Situations: a Non-Aggressive Approach'. I sensed the advent of a scathing denunciation, but Pickup suddenly seemed to check himself.

'A course, headmaster?' he questioned slowly, a gleam in his eye. 'Would that be over several days, then?'

'Yes, indeed, Pickup. Four days, to be precise, from 9 till 4–30 on each occasion.' Pickup smiled broadly as the head continued: 'Might give you a few insights into alternative methods of behaviour modification, eh?'

Aglow with apparent and unaccustomed enthusiasm, Pickup readily agreed: 'Mmm. Indeed. A great chance for some professional development – I'd be delighted to attend. You'll arrange all the necessary class cover, I presume?'

'Oh, that won't be necessary,' replied Mr Ross. 'It's on Saturdays.'

'Saturdays?' laughed Pickup. '*Saturdays?* But I thought you meant a week-day course. You don't honestly expect me to give up four Saturdays for a free show on how to deal with –'

'Oh, it's not free,' corrected the headmaster. 'There's a charge of £60 per head . . .'

'Sixty quid?'

'Well, yes. That includes a buffet lunch each day, you know.'

'I don't care if it includes wine, women and ruddy song! If you think I'm giving up four Saturdays to pay – to pay, mark you – for the privilege of attending a jumped-up in-service course, then you can think again, headmaster. Move it to a week-day, give me a proper sabbatical, and I'll think about it. But not until then!' spat Pickup, thrusting the course folder down and storming from the study.

I raised my eyes from the carpet whither they had been directed during Pickup's embarrassing tirade. Mr Ross looked towards me with a smile upon his face which I suspect he imagined to be encouraging. Reading the man's thoughts, I forestalled his immediate request by gathering the folder from his desk and telling him that I'd give the matter some serious consideration.

And perhaps I will.

October – November

Sadly, the provision of extra-curricular in-service courses was another area of teachers' professionalism which was severely disrupted during their protracted dispute over pay and conditions. In days past, it had been accepted practice that those teachers who wished to advance their professional development – and their careers – would attend such courses, often held after school on a weekday, sometimes – as we have seen – at a weekend.

Attendance was voluntary and unpaid, though a contribution towards travelling expenses would usually be made by the organising authority.

There were teachers enwrapped in cynicism who saw in these

courses an opportunity for a sycophantic demonstration of, at best, loyalty, or at worst, blatant careerism. There were others who saw in them an endless opportunity for college of education lecturers – who, more than occasionally, would be the begetters of such events – to justify their respective existences. Whatever the accuracy of such claims, it is nevertheless true that teachers who had hitherto attended such extra-curricular activities with a sense of willingness, a sense of 'give-and-take', now found themselves increasingly reluctant to devote any more of their time to work than that which was strictly laid down by contractual agreement with their employers.

Fortunately for the providers of such courses, however, there *were* still teachers willing enough, devoted enough, enthusiastic enough to give up their free time – and sometimes their money – to advance their professional development.

As the reader may already have guessed, and as the next diary entry reveals, Morris Simpson was such a teacher. The entry is also indicative of Simpson's continuing bewilderment over the innovatory policies being promoted by the new guard of educational reform: this time, the problem was over homework. To Morris, the eventual solution was unusual, to say the least. In this matter Mr Pickup was, as ever, a very present help in trouble – even if his advice regarding the control of conflict situations continued to border on the illegal.

Monday

A bitter dispute with one of my four first year classes this morning over their continued reluctance to complete homework. I have issued fourteen punishment exercises and another final warning.

An intriguing conversation over lunch with Mr Pickup of RE and geography wherein I revealed my reservations about the weekend staff-development course I've been attending recently: I *had* hoped that *Conflict Situations: A Non-Aggressive Approach* would provide me with a few practical guidelines on dealing with some of the more recalcitrant pupils under my charge. Our first two sessions, however, have been almost exclusively devoted to some particularly bland theorising from Mr Reckitt, the division's Adviser in Guidance. I explained my specific concern about Mr Reckitt's enthusiasm for what he fondly titles 'Introductory Group Dynamics'.

'Bloody hell!' exclaimed Pickup. 'Old Charlie's not still touting that one about, is he, Simpson?'

'Sorry?'

'His "Introductory Group Dynamics"? Charlie Reckitt's been flogging that particular horse since the days when even *I* was attending Guidance courses.'

'You attended –?'

'Mmm,' confirmed Pickup. 'But only on the condition he'd see me straight for a job thereafter.'

'So what happened?'

'Never finished the course, I'm afraid. Couldn't keep my face straight long enough. Every time we all met he'd start us off with a blindfold session of 'personal encounters' to help us get to know each other better.'

'Yes!' I confirmed. 'That's exactly what we were doing last Saturday afternoon. He claimed it would remove tension and facilitate interpersonal relationships.'

'The very thing!' laughed Pickup. 'Did it do you any good, then?'

'Not really,' I confessed. 'I'm afraid I found it all terribly embarrassing.'

'Me too. Wandered round the room for half an hour then found myself groping some woman's enormous backside from Cowglen.' Pickup sighed. 'That was my last meeting. Told Charlie Reckitt that if I wanted to get felt up I could think of more congenial surroundings and more attractive company to do it in.'

Privately reflecting that Pickup would never have proved a terribly sympathetic Guidance teacher in any case, I was about to leave the staffroom when he called me back.

'Listen, Simpson,' he leant towards me: 'if I were you I'd jack in the rest of this course. If you want some *really* effective pointers on how to deal with conflict in the classroom, take a gander at this . . .'

So saying, he withdrew a slim volume from the breast pocket of his blazer and pressed it into my hand. Its title – *Teach Yourself Self-Defence* – seemed to neatly encapsulate Pickup's attitude to education.

I'm not surprised he's never been properly promoted.

Tuesday

Very little time to compose a diary entry today: Tuesday is our recently instituted 'late-day', a session after 4 o'clock for some properly programmed in-service provision of real practical benefit. Unfortunately, its timing means that I am seldom home before 6–30 in the evening; normally, of course, I'm quite happy to devote a little extra time to professional development, but I found myself somewhat irritated by today's proceedings, most of which were devoted to a rectorial reading of a discussion document issued by the local education authority, a document improbably entitled 'Peace and War Studies in the School Curriculum'.

It didn't seem to bear much relevance to life at Parkland High, but the headmaster informed us that the education authorities had instructed us to discuss it, so discuss it we must. I suppose it filled a weary hour.

Wednesday

An angry meeting with our depute Mr Tod over my disciplinary dealings with 1F. The man has rescinded – and not for the first time in my teaching career – all of the punishment exercises which I issued on Monday.

His decision to do so was based, he explained, on the fact that I had directly contravened the school's homework policy, an allegation which I staunchly denied.

'Indeed?' queried Tod.

'Indeed!' I countered. 'If you'll take the trouble to examine my record of work, Mr Tod, I think you'll discover that every single class under my care has been issued with a regular and systematic diet of exercises to be completed at home. Furthermore, if you'll –'

Tod interrupted: 'Before you dig yourself any deeper, Mr Simpson, I'm afraid that's exactly the problem.'

'I don't understand.'

'No,' sighed the depute. 'I'm afraid you don't. Had you taken the trouble to read the school prospectus before rejoining us at the beginning of session, you'd have realised that we introduced a *new* homework policy this year.'

'Oh?'

'Yes.'

'And the difference?'

'The difference, Mr Simpson, is that the school's homework policy is not to *give* any homework.'

'Not to *give* any homework? But –'

'No,' the depute continued, sternly foreboding. 'We set up a sub-committee under the chairmanship of Miss Bowman and it came to the conclusion that homework merely exacerbated the differentials between children of higher and lower abilities. The good kids did the homework and got on faster; the toe-rags didn't and fell further behind. So we stopped homework altogether. And I'd advise you to do the same . . .'

Before I could frame a suitable reply, Mr Tod had disappeared in the direction of his office muttering darkly about 'examination returns for the S.E.B.'. Frankly, I wonder what education is coming to.

Thursday

I may have discovered a solution to the homework dilemma, and owe a deal of thanks to my mentor Mr Pickup. Despite confessing himself an avid devotee of the school's 'no homework' policy – 'if you don't give it, you don't have to mark it' – and announcing himself puzzled at my lack of enthusiasm for same, he has nevertheless come up with an ingenious proposal.

Put briefly, the solution springs from his firmly held conviction that educational innovation – no matter how unworthy – requires, in Pickup's own words, 'tarting up with a ridiculous name and some incomprehensible initials'. A gleam in his eye, he launched into the attack:

'Look at them all, Simpson: MSC, YTS, TVEI, YEP – all lined up to collect taxpayer's money and not doing a bloody bit of good for anyone in the process. Why don't you turn the tables?'

'Not quite with you, Pickup.'

'Look. For once, we've got a teacher actually trying to do something which'll *help* the kids under his charge. Except he's not allowed to do it. Until, that is, he comes up with a glossy proposal to satisfy the authorities that he's firmly in the vanguard of educational reform.'

I laughed. 'Any suggestions?'

'Yup. How about SBLP – *Subject Based Leisure Pursuits*? Homework by any other name, of course, but it's got all the necessary requirements: pretty grand to the ear, but completely nebulous to the brain.'

I admitted to initial scepticism, but Pickup was very convincing. He convinced me further over several pints of beer after school. I think I'll give it a try.

Friday

Pickup's suggestion has been more succesful than I could have possibly imagined! A final refinement to the scheme involved telling 1F, at Period 1, that no further homework would be given. Instead, I informed them, they had been specially selected to be the first class which would attempt a new module on Subject Based Leisure Pursuits. I stressed the exclusivity of the module and highlighted their unique position among my first year classes. With the exception of Angela Swift – a knowing little girl who eyed me suspiciously through the entire explanation – universal enthusiasm greeted the

26

chance to practise their 'communication-skills' by writing a letter to a pen friend when they got home.

By the end of the day, my module had become a firmly established aspect of the first year curriculum: every other class, on hearing of the privileges being accorded to 1F, was vehement in its demands for equal treatment.

'Aw, surr!' berated Tony Marshall of 1P, for example: 'It's no' ferr. How kin we no' get oan the SBLP modjul? Eh, sir? Eh?'

My feigned reluctance and eventual compliance would have done credit on stage, though I say so myself. I told them they could come aboard the module, but that they would have to start with only *one* 'home-skill assignment' per week until they had proved they could cope with more. Unmoved by their fervent complaints, I look forward to increasing their allocation next week.

Interestingly enough, even Mr Tod approves of the SBLP module. He seems to think it really *has* something to do with leisure pursuits and has congratulated me upon being the first teacher to involve myself in extra-curricular activities since the industrial action ceased. He went so far as to hint that the creation of such an impressive module would go a long way towards influencing the headmaster's attitude when he came to recommend me for full registration with the GTC.

Pickup, of course, thinks the whole matter hilarious and has suggested I apply for an urban aid grant to help finance the programme. I told him not to be ridiculous but our afternoon session in the local hostelry gave me cause to ponder anew. Perhaps it's not such a silly idea after all . . .

December

It was difficult for any teacher in the late 1980s, young or old, to keep up with the bewildering array of teaching novelties which could emanate from educational researchers. A 'no-homework' policy based on the same awkward premise as Parkland High's was not at all an uncommon practice, and the fact that Mr Tod so easily accepted the existence of such a ridiculously acronymed 'SBLP Module' speaks volumes for the confusion which so densely shrouded the educational service. It also spoke volumes for Mr Tod's grip on reality, which had never been more than slender.

There were some things, however, which had always been part of everyday school life, and which were likely to remain so. Termly reports, for example, would always seem to be assured of a place in every teacher's heart, especially in the approach to the Christmas holidays, when so many other events make an appearance in an already crowded timetable. Late assessments, long lists of class-names, last minute holiday preparations all contribute to the difficulty of making accurate grading and behavioural judgements regarding individual pupils. Not everybody, it will be seen, gave as much careful thought to their Christmas reports as Morris Simpson.

And then, what school Christmas would be complete without the end-of-term nativity play? An event more naturally associated with primary schools, Morris nevertheless found himself enjoined with Mr Pickup in Parkland High's attempt to provide a dramatic, modernised presentation of the greatest story ever told. It was a bold venture.

Monday

An extremely busy week ahead: the first year reports are due in by tomorrow and, with four first year classes, I am finding difficulty in meeting the deadline. In addition, Mr Pickup and I have foolishly acceded to the seasonal requests of my sixth year O grade repeat class that they 'pit oan a Christmas gig': having enlisted, then, the assistance of my colleague from RE in an attempt to impress the headmaster with some interdisciplinary liaison, we decided to produce a latter day nativity play for the benefit of paying customers and assorted councillors on Thursday evening. It's based largely on a text which Pickup dredged up from one of his class books and will go by the somewhat unlikely title of 'If Jesus Came To Parkland High'.

I admit to initial unease about the entire venture, but it certainly seems to be giving the sixth year a purpose in life: a group of chronic underachievers, they seldom have interest in school work, but the prospect of public performance seems to have filled them with enthusiasm. The only area of serious contention was casting. We had litle choice other than to give the two principal parts to the most voluble members of the class, the boy Sinnot and the girl Rose McShane. The improbable sight of the school's most violently anti-social pupils portraying Joseph and Mary should at least convince the headmaster of my abilities to draw the best from difficult pupils under my charge.

Pickup, ever the cynic, couldn't help but observe that the role of an unmarried mother should fit Rose well for the future, but I've told him to put himself in the Christmas spirit and stop carping. The girl looked positively beatific in rehearsal this afternoon; I just hope it lasts.

Tuesday

A trying and frustrating day. Having spent all of my lunch hour completing the first year report sheets in the ladies' staffroom, I found myself unable to locate marks for Simon Freebairn of class

1G. Normally meticulous in my assessment records, I was extremely concerned to have lost all apparent documentation of the boy's progress; indeed, I couldn't actually remember anything about the child in the first place. Further investigation, however, revealed that the fault did not lie at my door.

To explain, it appears that young Simon was a placing request at the beginning of session; however, after two days under our educational ministrations, he elected to place his custom elsewhere and transferred out. Unfortunately, his name was never removed from 1G's assessment register, hence my confusion.

It nevertheless came as something of a surprise to me that no fewer than *eight* of my colleagues had already filled in assessments for a non-existent pupil! Pickup, for example, had described him as an 'able and enthusiastic student of religious education' and had recommended that he think seriously of taking an O grade, while Mr Douglas of history had made a similarly enthusiastic appraisal. Meanwhile, Mr Dunbar of maths had suggested a little extra practice with investigative approaches. Miss Honeypot of PE had, alas, found little time for additional written comment but, by ticking the relevant boxes, had discovered young Simon to be 'competent' in all areas of physical activity – a judgement which, upon further investigation, she appears to have made with regard to each of 1G's 31 pupils!

This revelation served only to heighten the doubts I have harboured about the professionalism of my colleagues, and I lost little time in reporting the register's anomaly to Mr Major, the AHT who is rumoured to be in charge of such matters. Unfortunately, consultation of his *own* documents revealed Simon Freebairn to be a model pupil whose attendance record was beyond reproach ('Well,' he explained patiently, 'he's never been marked *absent*, y'see . . .').

Major has promised to destroy the fictitious report and amend his own records. For my own part, I am left wondering exactly what he *does* to earn a responsibility allowance.

Wednesday

Hectic preparations for the play tomorrow night. Owing to some last minute withdrawals by the sixth year, I find myself short of ten extra shepherds and have had to draft in some first-year boys. They don't have much to say, but it's meant the provision of extra scripts and some very quick coaching.

Armed, therefore, with a copy of Pickup's book and fifty sheets of paper, my attempts to enter the photocopying office were nevertheless hampered by the presence of a book representative who had just arrived. The awkward little man seemed intent upon displaying his wares on every available surface of an already overcrowded room.

'Morning,' I smiled, in a vain effort to squeeze myself between his display and the feeder tray. He seemed to take the hint, and transferred a case of books to an opposite shelf.

Having enquired of me which subject I taught, he launched into an ill-prepared monologue concerning the benefits of his company's recently published English course, but I cut him short:

'I'm sorry,' I cut in, 'but I really haven't the time. In the first place, I don't have the authority to spend any money; in the second, even if I did we haven't *got* any; and in the third, this is completely the wrong time of year for you people to come round. Imagine. The week before Christmas and a commercial traveller arrives! Do you really think anyone's got the *time* to come and look at a book display at this time of year?'

I may have spoken rather harshly, for he seemed to blanch at the term 'commercial traveller', and muttered something about having to make a living, but I think I put him in his place. In any case, he transferred his attention to my own activities at the photocopier and asked if we were putting on a show.

I gave him a brief run-down of the problems associated with our forthcoming production, not least the extra expense of having to copy ten more scripts on top of the twenty-four already produced, and he apologised for having inconvenienced me at such an obviously awkward time.

As the copier spat out its final script, I gathered the sheets together, accepted his apology, and bade him a courteous farewell. Final rehearsal tonight.

Thursday

An embarrassment. A calamity. An unmitigated disaster.

I refer, of course, to the sixth year's (and first year's) production of 'If Jesus Came to Parkland High'. The opening scene, intended to create an air of transcendental mystery as a group of shepherds crossed an urban landscape, was met with guffaws of disbelief from an audience whose attention was understandably distracted by the fact that the costumes designed for our original shepherds were hopelessly large for 1F's Tony Greig and Sammy Marshall.

31

My concern was heightened by the first appearance of Joseph and Mary. The latter, in particular, seemed to need excessive prompting and had a definite tendency to slur her words together. Her attempts to rouse the 'hotel porter' (the play's modern-day equivalent of an innkeeper) owed more to Rose McShane's vivid imagination than any close adherence to the script:

'Haw youse!' she bellowed at the hotel's shuttered window. 'Goanny get oot yur kip, ya wee diddy?'

Matters went from bad to worse as she forcibly negotiated a bed and breakfast rate for herself and Joseph. The said gentleman, meanwhile, appeared to have lost all interest in proceedings and fell to gazing aimlessly into space. He seemed to be having difficulty focusing his eyes . . .

The interval curtain afforded momentary relief, and a chance to investigate matters further. My way to the dressing room, however, was barred by a frantic first-year pupil who refused to grant access.

'Ye canny go in there, surr. Ye canny.'

'What d'you mean, boy,' I snapped. 'Get out of my way.'

'But ye canny,' he repeated, before making an announcement whose echoes will reverberate, I feel certain, throughout my teaching career. An arm across the doorway, his pre-pubescent voice squeaked a proclamation of limitless consequence: 'The Vurgin Mary, surr. She's drunk, surr . . .'

'What! Drunk? But –?'

'Aye. An' Joseph an' a'. Absolutely guttered, surr . . . !'

And so it proved. The awesome burden of their respective stage débuts had all been too much for Rose and Sinnot. Entry once gained to the dressing room, the remnants of an entire bottle of vodka and three cans of lager were discovered to have been shared by our starring couple, both now oblivious to the outside world and sprawled lovingly in each other's arms. Needless to say, they could take no further part in the performance and we cancelled the second half with an announcement of 'circumstances beyond our control'.

The headmaster looked furious. I suspect he'll want to see me tomorrow.

Friday

As expected, a request from the headmaster to present myself in his study at the earliest opportunity.

'Look, headmaster,' I launched, 'I'm most awfully sorry about last night. It was a terrible –'

'Yes, Simpson,' Mr Ross predicted my description. 'It certainly was. But that's not what I'm worried about at present.'

My heart leapt. 'No?'

'No. It's this.' He held a letter in his hand and spoke very, very quietly, menace in his voice. My heart sank.

'Oh, headmaster?'

'Yes, Simpson. It's a letter.'

'A letter, headmaster?'

'A letter from a publisher, Simpson. He seems rather concerned about photocopying.'

'Photocopying, headmaster?'

'Yes, Simpson. It seems that one of his representatives witnessed a member of our staff producing multiple copies of a playscript. Multiple copies of a playscript to perform for a paying audience, no less. And multiple copies of a playscript which is, in fact, published by his company. Do you know how he knew that, Simpson?'

My voice shook. 'No, headmaster?'

Mr Ross filled his lungs and let fly: 'Because the stupid oaf responsible left the ruddy book in the machine!' he bawled.

'Ah. Would that be me, headmaster?'

'Of course it's you!' he bellowed. 'My God, Simpson, does your imbecility really know no bounds? First of all you fearlessly churn out a mountain of illegal photocopies in front of a publisher's rep and then – according to this letter – you see fit to insult the man so gratuitously that he shops us to his boss!'

'I'm sorry, headmaster, but –'

'Never mind sorry, Mr Simpson. Just start thinking about a lawyer, that's all.'

'A lawyer? But –?'

'Yes, a lawyer!' Mr Ross waved the letter in my face. 'The buggers are taking us to court!'

Dejection in my heart, I stumbled from the headmaster's study, my dreams of GTC registration crumbling about me. So much for Christmas spirit.

January

Morris had a depressing festive break, his thoughts overshadowed by the constant spectre of legal action which, the headmaster had promised, was bound to follow his unfortunate disagreement with the publisher's representative.

January came and went, however, and he heard nothing further about it. Blissfully unaware that the wheels of justice grind even more slowly than those of educational administration, he adjudged the matter closed, and redirected his energies into giving of his best to the young charges under his care. He was especially keen to encourage a more dedicated response from his social education class, who seemed to tire easily of the topics which the school guidance course provided for them. Morris, with an eventual eye on the possibilities of promotion within the guidance sector, was keen to make an impression in the field.

It was difficult, of course, to maintain *any* interest from his classes when their attentions were so frequently diverted by the living streams of water which cascaded around the walls of Hut A57. The rains of January were giving credence to Morris's prophetic fears of the previous autumn, for his flat roof was singularly unable to withstand the rigours of a Scottish winter.

It is still a source of puzzlement to many commentators that flat roofs maintained their popularity with school architects for such an astonishingly long time. Having first made a somewhat ugly – but cheap – appearance on the scene of school construction in the 1960s, it was well into the 1980s before new schools began to be equipped with sloping roofs once more. Meanwhile, twenty five years of misguided building policy had left a legacy of schools with continual and continuous leakage problems. A walk through the top-floor accommodation of just about any Scottish school built during this period will frequently reveal a sorry trail of buckets, basins and soggy mops, a visible testament to architects' repeated assurances that flat roofs would be a perfectly adequate form of protection if the covering material was applied correctly. Apparently, it seldom was.

Simpson's diary extract for the end of January tells the rest of the story.

Monday

Some worrying leaks have appeared in the flat roof of the hut which I share with Mr Pickup (religious education and geography). The inclement weather of recent weeks has necessitated strategic placement of several large buckets on the floor, a tremendous inconvenience during any lessons which incorporate dramatic improvisation. In addition, large quantities of water are flowing in close proximity to the electrical installations, causing me serious concern about potentially fatal accidents. Pickup, apparently oblivious, intends to take advantage of the conditions to mount a project on post-diluvian conditions in the Old Testament.

I have urged Mr Crichton, our janitor, for immediate action from the region's works department and he tells me they have given the matter a 'top priority' grading. Apparently, this grading is only utilised when the fabric would constitute a danger to health if left unrepaired, so I fully expected a visitation from the builders by late afternoon, and was rather surprised to discover their non-appearance by 4 pm.

'This'll mean some expensive overtime tonight,' I commented to Pickup as we gazed at the steady flow of water coursing down our partition.

'Hah!' he guffawed. 'Tonight? Don't kid yourself, sonny. Top priority, eh?'

'Yes. And Mr Crichton said that –'

'Look. Never mind Andy Crichton. This roof could disintegrate round our ears any minute, but we'll see neither hide nor hair of any contractors until – um,' – he paused in reflection – 'Friday at the earliest. I guarantee it.'

I sometimes grow weary of Pickup's cynical outlook, and on this occasion told him so.

'Mark my words, Simpson,' he muttered darkly. 'And bring your wellies tomorrow.'

Tuesday

A minor disciplinary problem with my first-year social education class. A vociferous minority had announced an unwillingness to embark upon any further project work about 'that wee nun'. I confess to a certain degree of shock at their grossly disrespectful reference to Mother Teresa, upon whom the current unit is based, but once again took the problem to my neighbourly mentor at coffee break.

'Ah yes,' he chortled. 'That's old Major's guidance course, isn't it?'

I confirmed that I was indeed following the outlines prepared by our assistant head as part of his remit for curriculum development.

'Yup,' continued Pickup: 'that's the one he pinched from his pal at St Ainsley's.'

'What!' I exclaimed. 'You mean he didn't make it up himself?'

'Well,' he conceded, 'he did go to the trouble of blanking out 'St Ainsley's High School' at the top of every page and inserting 'Parkland High' instead. Other than that,' he concluded, 'I suspect you'll find that *our* social education course bears an almost identical resemblance to that provided by our Roman Catholic brethren up the road.'

'So *that's* why . . .' I began.

'Mmm,' mused Pickup, eyes in the distance: 'Sixteen weeks of Mother Teresa, eh?'

'Well, they do seem to be growing rather tired of it,' I admitted. 'Any suggestions?'

'Tell it not to the Board of Management,' he whispered conpiratorially, 'but if I were you I'd move straight on to sex.'

'Sorry?'

'Sex: it's the only thing in that bloody awful course that *I* could ever get them interested in. That should keep you going until Easter, and most of them start skiving off soon after that.'

I pondered the ramifications as Pickup rinsed out his coffee mug.

'Mind you,' he added in apparent afterthought: 'if you're still working from St Ainsley's course, there's a fair bit of *that* section needs altering as well. Especially the bits on birth control.' Eyebrows raised, he sauntered from the room.

Wednesday

A 'please-take' for Miss Denver, head of history and absent on Standard grade development work. Normally I find such requests rather tiresome, but this one at least occasioned the chance to escape the rapidly deteriorating conditions in Hut A57. Pickup's advice about wellingtons has not been as foolish as I'd first imagined.

Anyway, there was little effort involved in conducting Miss Denver's first year class as they were due to be given an assessment on their 'knowledge and understanding' of the first term's work.

I have to admit a strong sense of outrage at the ridiculously low standards attained by some of the pupils – it's certainly not the kind of work I'd accept in my own clasroom. If they are to be believed, however, many of these children profess to love history because they're so good at it! And the questions in their test seemed incredibly easy!

Mr Pringle, my elderly departmental colleague, saw nothing unusual in the matter.

'It's the options, y'see,' he informed me when I brought the matter up after lunch.

'Sorry?'

'The options. Give me a child until the end of second year – and he's mine for life.'

'I'm sorry, Mr Pringle?'

'Oh, for goodness' sake, Simpson – and people tell me that *I'm* slowing up! Miss Denver,' he explained patiently, 'is in the process of winning souls.'

'Winning souls?'

'Yes. To those of us whose subjects enjoy the luxury of entire columns to themselves in the third year options it is, perhaps, a strange concept. But out there in the marketplace,' his voice hardened, 'it can be tough as hell.'

Still bewildered, I requested further elucidation. Pringle went on to relate the most fantastic theory that Miss Denver and her geographical counterpart, Mr Crumley, spend most of their waking hours in a curricular battle to persuade the junior school to take up their respective subjects as they progress to senior examinations. A substantial part of the strategy, according to Pringle, is to heap eloquent tributes of ability on to every pupil's head in an effort to persuade him or her that they actually excel at the subject in question. Apparently, he claims, even the stupidest boy in first year is normally expected to emerge from termly assessments with an 'A' grading in both history *and* geography.

'But that's ridiculous!' I complained. 'Apart from the sheer dishonesty involved, what on earth happens once they get to third year and –'

'Aha,' confirmed Pringle: 'That's when the *real* work starts. And that's when they start streaming them.'

'Streaming! Surely not. Not in this day and age. They can't –'

Pringle interrupted me with a look of baleful scorn and continued his pathetic attempts to justify such unconscionable lowering of educational standards in the junior school. Half an hour later, he had me convinced.

I wonder if the headmaster knows what's going on?

Thursday

I seem to have made some enemies in the social studies department. Mr Ross was apparently unaware of the creative assessment techniques being utilised by the history and geography departments in his school. It had never been my intention to reveal the matter to him, but our weekly discussion of my probationary progress saw him launch his accustomed attack on the academic gradings attained by pupils under my charge. I foolishly let slip a remark about 'not cooking the books' and he pounced like a panther.

In brief, the whole sordid saga emerged. By the time I left his study, Mr Crumley and Miss Denver were awaiting entry. They emerged thirty minutes later, when the malevolence of their expressions towards each other was equalled only by the sheer and consuming hatred of the glares aimed in my direction.

Goodness knows why. I'm only thinking of the kids.

Roof much worse. I have donned a sou'ester for lessons: sometimes it seems wetter inside than out . . .

Friday

The eventual arrival of the roofing contractors unfortunately coincided with my intention of playing some reflective music to class

1F as a peaceful stimulus to creative writing. Unfortunately, my soporific recording of *Berceuse de Jocelyn* was punctuated by ungainly footsteps above and the inelegantly phrased requests of a young apprentice to 'chuck us that fuckin' hammer, wull ye'.

'At least,' I consoled Mr Pickup at break, 'it'll all be over soon and we can get back to normality.'

'Don't you believe it,' he contradicted. 'This is only the start.'

'The start?'

'Uh-huh. They'll fix it today, but it'll be too damp to effect a permanent repair. They need dry weather to sort it properly, and the reason it's leaking so much is precisely because we haven't *had* any dry weather since Christmas. I reckon it should start letting in again by next Thursday at the latest. So they'll be back a fortnight later to effect *another* temporary repair, complete with transistor radios and swearing navvies. Normal routine after that is monthly visits until June – great fun in June, of course: that's when they really go to town with their gas cylinders and their blowtorches. Marvellous: the only time of year you need to have all the windows open and Joe Bloggs marches on to your roof with a deafening roar and an outburst of poisonous tar fumes.'

'But why can't they do it during the holidays?'

'One of life's great mysteries, Simpson. Sure as fate, though, they'll pack up tools on the 30th June, stamp the job finished, and leave the place bereft of noise all through the summer. Come August 18th, though, you'll see them lining up at the school gates ready to come and fix an extra layer of 'winter protection' and to spend the next eight weeks tramping around your ceiling like a herd of mating elephants.'

'You mean this has happened before?'

'Of course. It happens every year, and it'll go on happening until some bright spark in the regional offices decides to build a roof with a slope on it.' He jerked a thumb upwards: 'It'd soon put these buggers out of work, mind.'

We both contemplated the highly discoloured ceiling above us and the filthily stained walls around us. Pickup's eyes narrowed as his thoughts seemed to centre on the trials, tribulations and discomforts we've had to endure in recent weeks and which, by his account, will continue in future months. His anger seemed to simmer – and then it exploded:

'And all because,' he erupted across the room at me, 'the culmination of mankind's constructional ingenuity in this country is to continue shoving flat roofs on buildings when any remedial half-wit can tell they're no bloody use!' The pitch of his voice rose with animated fury as he strove towards a final condemnation: 'Just think of it! Two thousand years of civilisation – and we've still got pea-brained architects who can't get it into their thick heads that flat roofs hold water *in* while sloping ones let it *run away*!'

Staring into my coffee mug, I adjusted my waterproof trousers, nodded in quiet agreement, and made no comment. Pickup seems to feel quite strongly about the matter.

February

In many schools the month of February sees the advent of preliminary examinations – 'prelims', for short. These annual forerunners of the genuine article, the Scottish Certificate of Education examinations in April and May, serve to give some approximation of likely future performance. They also serve, for English teachers in particular, to give an unusually heavy marking load during subsequent weeks.

It was perhaps for this reason, and no other, that Angela Bowman decided to allocate a small section of O grade marking to the least experienced member of her department. It was with some measure of uncertainty that she eventually decided to let Morris mark the fourth year's compositions, believing him least likely to do any serious damage in this section of the paper. Sadly, her decision was the source of some fairly serious professional disagreement with Morris, whose ideas about competent writing were not entirely in tune with modern methodology.

For Morris, of course, it was a chance to prove himself, and he approached the task with unbridled enthusiasm. Unfortunately, the first week of March also saw the arrival of a publisher's letter adressed to the headmaster: it imparted some serious news of a legal nature . . .

41

Monday

An overcrowded week ahead. I am distressed to report that the matter of a litigious publisher has returned to haunt me, following an ill-advised foray to the photocopier before Christmas, wherein I foolishly allowed a visiting publisher's rep to witness an industrious session of illegal photocopying. His employer's promise to initiate proceedings against the school appears to have been no idle threat, and I find myself the object of continuing rectorial scorn from Mr Ross, subsequent to his receiving further legal correspondence this morning.

Miss Bowman, my head of department, consoles me with the suggestion that the regional authorities will arrive at a solution and urges that I devote attention instead to the mountainous accumulation of 'prelim' exam papers requiring my attention. I must admit to a certain degree of pride in being allowed to mark O grade papers for the first time in my career: although for only one section of the paper (composition), it is an obvious mark of Miss Bowman's increasing trust in my professional judgement. I don't intend to let her down.

Tuesday

A double free-period this morning at last afforded me the opportunity to make a concerted effort at the prelim papers. I confess to a large measure of astonishment at the appallingly low standards of presentation by candidates, most particularly in the areas of punctuation and spelling. The illiterate contributions of my own sixth year class (sitting the exam for the third time) provided, of course, little surprise, but I was frankly dismayed my the frequent inability of even the top section in fourth year (Miss Bowman's class) to compose properly constructed sentences. Indeed, so inept have been the majority of submissions that I have yet to award a single pass mark. Standards, after all, have to be maintained.

I mentioned the matter to Mr Pickup during what has become our regular 4 o'clock visit to The Pig and Whistle but he seemed strangely disinterested in my assessment problems.

'Mmm?' he raised an eyebrow as he ordered a second pint of beer. 'Fancy that, now . . .'

I surmised that I didn't have his full attention and offered a penny for his thoughts.

'Eh?'

'A penny. For your thoughts, old man.'

'Oh,' he brightened up. 'Nothing really. Just this afternoon's visit from the AA.'

'Automobile Asso –?'

'No, no,' Pickup laughed. 'Alcoholics Anonymous.'

'Not a personal visitation, I trust?'

'Ach, of course not,' he scoffed. 'They were here for an input to social and moral education for the third-year guidance slot.'

'And . . . ?' I probed.

Pickup was unusually reluctant to continue, but further enquiry revealed that the AA's homily, though mainly aimed at an adolescent audience, had found an unusually accurate target in the said audience's religious education teacher. 'Bloody hell, Simpson,' Pickup elaborated: 'd'you know what they said about the "unmistakeable signs of alcoholism"?'

I requested elaboration, and was not entirely surprised to learn that, of the ten major indicators of incipient alcoholism outlined in the Association's talk, Pickup claimed to fulfil all but one.

'And which one's that?' I queried.

'Can't do without a drink after work,' he explained gloomily. 'At least I've not fallen into that one yet . . .'

I pursed my lips as Pickup ordered another pint of beer and suggested a pineapple juice instead, but he fixed me with a baleful glare and suggested I mind my own business.

Perhaps I should keep an eye on him.

Wednesday

A furious row with Miss Bowman over O grade marking procedures. My strict refusal to countenance anything other than the highest standards of grammatical presentation has been met with an unconscionable willingness by my head of department to accede to the general *lowering* of such standards!

A case in point. Aileen Fraser's attempt to write a composition based on her enthusiastic appreciation of a recent pop concert was fatally flawed by her constant and repeated reluctance to award new sentences the distinction of a capital letter at their beginnings, as well as a pointed refusal to signal the end of any previous sentence with a full stop. Consequently, it became increasingly difficult to elicit any kind of sensible meaning from her writings: in effect, she had presented me with a badly spelled, one sentence composition of approximately six hundred words! Yet when I presented my completed allocation of marking to Miss B this afternoon, she found fault with practically every script and, in Ailen Fraser's case, insisted I change the mark from an 'E' grading to a 'B'.

'You can't be serious!' I protested.

'Of course I'm serious,' she replied tartly. 'Aileen Fraser's put a *tremendous* amount of effort into this composition and we have to reward her in some way; the imaginative creativity she's displayed is almost worthy of an 'A' grade, in my opinion.'

'But she's not written in *sentences* . . .'

'Look, Morris,' Miss B explained patiently, 'it's not about sentences.'

'No?'

'No. It's about sensitivity. And Aileen Fraser's demonstrated an abundance of that. What we're trying to teach them in English these days is to give free and unfettered reign to their thoughts. Some of these kids . . .' she noticed me blanch at the terminology, but repeated: 'some of these kids lead lives of indescribable boredom and deprivation. It's as much as some of them can do to string three *words* together in coherent expression, let alone three sentences. In the light of that, Aileen Fraser's composition is an epic of towering imagination! You're looking at all the *negative* aspects instead of the positive ones. It's all about *positive* marking, Morris.'

'But that's the point. I couldn't find anything positive about it.'

'Nonsense,' she rejoined. 'Look closely enough in that composition, and you'll find thought processes and imagery which are way beyond anything we'd –'

I resisted. 'But you can't read it! Most of it's illegible and the rest doesn't make sense!'

'It's all about positive marking, Morris,' she repeated. 'You've got to give these kids a chance . . .'

That settled it. The papers are due back tomorrow. I have refused to alter a single mark.

Thursday

A blazing row with Miss Bowman this afternoon, five minutes after handing back the O grade prelim papers to my sixth-year repeat class. Having assumed a suitably stern expression prior to the distribution of papers, and having prepared an equally suitable diatribe concerning the appalling standard of work, I was somewhat taken aback to discover Rose McShane, the enormously framed girl with severe learning difficulties, wearing a grin of beatific proportions.

'I suppose you think your mark's funny, young lady?' I enquired.

'Naw, naw, surr,' she replied. 'Ah'm just dead chuffed!'

'I beg your pardon?'

'Chuffed, surr. Ah've nivir hud a 'C' grade afore.'

'Yes, well, perhaps that'll make you put some effort into –' I caught myself short. 'What did you say?'

'Ah said ah've nivir had . . .'

'Yes, yes, I heard you. Give me your paper.'

Detailed investigation revealed that Miss Bowman had been through every ruddy paper and, contrary to all of the strictures in my carefully devised marking scheme, had upped all marks by an average rate of thirty five per cent, irrespective of literary merit. In the particular case of Rose McShane, my own written comments had been to the effect that her composition was devoid of any discernible content other than a title and a semi-obscene limerick; Miss Bowman, for her part, had seen fit to encourage the girl for a 'novel approach to the question' and then to suggest she extend her talent for poetic expression.

I have told Miss Bowman that I find her approach contrary to all professional ethics and have suggested that I may put in for a transfer. She doesn't seem unduly concerned.

Friday

Departmental relations approached an all-time nadir this afternoon with the headmaster's announcement that an agreement had been reached with the publishers of the illegally photocopied book. As a gesture of goodwill they have agreed to drop court proceedings and accept an out of court settlement as a token gesture.

'Some goodwill,' muttered Mr Ross to me at afternoon break. 'And some gesture. We're still talking about a large sum of money, Simpson – and we're still talking about the regional authority not coughing up.'

'Which means, headmaster . . . ?'

'Which means, Mr Simpson, that the cash will have to come out of our normal *per capita* allocation.'

'I see. I'd like to help out, headmaster, but it's not very feasible on my salary. In a sense, I suppose it was partly my fault . . .'

'*Partly* your fault?' he exploded across his study. '*Partly* your fault? It was *all* your ruddy fault, Simpson, and don't you forget it!

45

'Which is why,' he continued in slightly calmer vein, 'I have decided to remove the sum concerned from the English department's allocation in the approaching financial year.'

I temporarily forgot myself: 'But you can't do that. It's nearly half our total budget, and Miss Bowman will –'

'It's *precisely* half your total budget, you half-wit, which is why I suggested it as an appropriate sum to the publishers. And I can do whatever I *like* with the allocations. The way I feel towards the English department at present, and the valiant efforts of one of its members to bankrupt the entire bloody school,' he glanced sharply over his desk at me, 'you can count yourself lucky I don't shut the whole caboodle down. As far as I can see, you don't even teach them to read and write properly.'

I thought it wiser not to bring up the question of my principled stand over the prelim marks and accepted his peremptory wave of dismissal.

Fortunately, I managed to avoid Miss Bowman for the rest of the afternoon, though I did catch sight of her in animated conversation with the headmaster at 4 o'clock. I decided not to join them, instead accepting Pickup's invitation for a quick one at The Pig and Whistle.

We stayed until closing time.

46

March

Only eight months into his restarted teaching career, Morris Simpson was already beginning to remember why he had left it in the first place.

Aside from the everyday problems of educational mayhem which he seemed to attract, he was also distressed by the 'new wave' of educational reform as demonstrated by Miss Bowman's enthusiasm for creativity at the expense of clarity. What was the point, he wondered, of encouraging pupils to express themselves at will if they were not disciplined in the rigidity of thought so necessary to convey proper meaning, as evinced in correct spelling and adequate grammatical construction? Similarly, could he really believe that the history and geography departments were engaged in a long-term battle over potential exam candidates by offering a wide array of glittering prizes, rather than simply trying to teach the facts about their respective subjects, as had been the case in his own, dearly remembered school days?

And even, he realised in his diary entry for March, the fond memories which he held for the traditional, balanced school dinner were soon to be a thing of the past. The provision of school meals was to be put out to competitive tender, and Parkland's local authority aimed to ensure that the fare which they offered proved to be more attractive – and more cost-effective – than hitherto, by providing a cafeteria-style menu of filled rolls, chips and a devastating array of sweetmeats, from which the pupils would choose at will. Any potential losses in nutritional value, it was felt, would be more than offset by the financial success of any such venture, for it was reckoned that the customers would jump at the chance of consuming endless quantities of hamburgers, chips and the like. Sadly for Morris, this assessment of teenage appetites proved accurate.

And yet, for such an apparent traditionalist, Morris Simpson had an occasional enthusiasm for the new. Ever willing to open his mind to the possible benefits of new curricular areas – and possible sources of promotion – he had tried, unsuccessfully, to initiate a media studies course in Parkland High ever since he had first joined the staff. The depute head had taken some convincing about the validity of such a course but, at last, he seemed willing to relent. As April began, Morris sensed a chance of victory.

Monday

Today saw the culmination of a long-running battle with Mr Tod, our depute head, when he at last conceded an allocation of time for my media studies course next session. This is something I've been trying to get off the ground for some months, and Tod has needed some fairly stiff arguments to convince him of the serious intent behind the course. He hasn't much idea about modern teaching ideas, I'm afraid.

Unfortunately, I still remain out of favour with Miss Bowman, my head of department, over the 50 per cent cut in the English department's requisition money, a draconian measure imposed by the headmaster in payment of damages to the publisher whose textbook I inadvertently photocopied before Christmas. Indeed, Mr Ross's strictures about economy seem to be making themselves felt in all aspects of school life, not least the lunch hall. Today saw the implementation of a new cafeteria-style management – and menu – in the school's dining facilities, and I confess to a strong measure of disapproval upon presenting myself at the serving hatch this afternoon.

'Usual, please, Mrs Bond,' I requested: 'Steak, two veg., and a portion of apple crumble. Without custard, if you please..'

'Sorry, Mr Simpson. They're all off.'

'Ah. Never mind. Give me . . . um . . . a cold meat salad, then, and –'

'Sorry. That's off, too. Filled rolls, chips, beans, chocolate cake, jammy biscuits or millionaire shortbread. That's about it, I'm afraid. We've been run off our feet since lunch-time started.'

'And you've run out of steak and veg already?'

'No. We never had them on in the first place.'

'What? But you *always* have steak and veg, Mrs Bond –'

'Not any more, Mr Simpson. It's the new system, you see. The kids don't want steak and veg; they want crisps and cola or chocolate and cherryade. And with the contract going up for tender next year, we've got to move into the market place.'

I was about to query the nutritional content of such offerings when the hugely proportioned Rose McShane lurched past, clutching her main meal of the day – a plate of chips and two packets of crisps. Pausing only to swathe the chips in a virulent shade of tomato ketchup, she caught my eye and, her acne-ridden features aglow with satisfaction, beamed an all-encompassing smile in my direction.

'School dinners is rerr, surr. Intit?'

The appraisal complete, she thrust a handful of chips into an already over-burdened mouth and waddled away to join some friends at the cola-bar.

I shuddered quietly and left the dining hall.

Tuesday

A day of exciting challenge.

I've hit upon a brilliant scheme to alleviate the nutritional vandalism being perpetrated by Mrs Bond's new dining system; in addition, it should improve my standing with Miss Bowman.

'A health food tuck-shop!' I declared to Mr Pickup at afternoon break. 'It's perfect. I'll set up a health food stall outside the dining room and give the pupils a chance to eat some decent food instead of the institutionalised cholesterol they're being served up by the new régime.'

'How d'you mean 'health food', Simpson?' queried Pickup.

'Health food. You know – raisins, nuts, cheese, brown fibre rolls, that kind of thing. I'm going to do it with my sixth year as part of their social and vocational skills programme: we're selling healthy snacks every Friday lunchtime as an alternative to the official school fare – and all the profit goes to English department funds'

Pickup laughed. 'So you aim to make a profit out of all this?'

'Oh yes. Mr Tod's very keen on the notion. He's decided to call it an Enterprise Skills Project and –'

'A *what*?'

'An Enterprise Skills Project. He says it should look pretty good in next year's prospectus . . .'

'Good God!' snorted Pickup. 'To think it should come to this, that we're financing the English requisition with sales of cheese rolls and monkey nuts –'

I cut him short. 'If you've any constructive suggestions to make, Mr Pickup, I'll be glad to hear them. Otherwise, I'll be pleased to see you first in the queue on Friday lunchtime!'

Sometimes I tire of Pickup's constant attempts to stifle initiative. At least Mr Tod favours the scheme: he's even seen fit to offer us a grant from school funds to finance the initial costs.

Wednesday

Mr Tod's ambivalent attitude towards me was amply illustrated this afternoon when he reneged on his media studies promise. Yesterday the blue-eyed boy over my Enterprise Skills development, today I found myself the object of his impassioned scorn during a heated discussion in the television room.

The problem arose after I had completed viewing a recorded programme with class 1F on the deconstruction of televisual imagery. Although my planned media course won't start until next year, I had thought it a good starting point, though much of the material did seem to go over their heads. Period four had ten minutes to run, however, and we found ourselves with some spare time on our hands.

'Surr!' pleaded Michael Evans: 'Goanny let us watch *Neyburrs*? Eh, surr? Goanny?'

'Aye, c'moan, surr,' chimed in Maureen Kent. 'Ah've missed it yisterday. It's great, surr, sure it is?'

Further enquiry led me to understand that, if I tuned in quickly enough, we could catch the last ten minutes of an Australian soap opera which assumes enormous popularity with class 1F and which is broadcast in both the early and late afternoon. Imbued with a certain degree of curiosity about their leisure viewing, I acceded to their demands and switched channels as an end-of-period treat. The programme's contents proved something of a revelation, for it seemed to consist solely of scantily clad adults and teenagers embroiled in a series of highly-charged relationships.

Sadly, I soon found myself engrossed in the climactic scenes of what appeared to be a particularly torrid episode; so much so, in fact, that I failed to hear the period bell and, worse still, failed to notice Mr Tod awaiting entry with his fifth-year social education class.

'So, Mr Simpson,' he bellowed from the back of the darkened room: 'This is media studies, is it? Soft pornography with the first year, eh?'

'What's that?' I peered into the darkness. 'Who's there?'

'Never mind who's here, Simpson. Just get your class out and let mine in. And come and see me later, please . . .'

Over and above the disgraceful lack of respect which the depute accorded me in front of my own class, I was furious that he had jumped to such a suspicious conclusion. My protests availed nought, however, for our 4 o'clock meeting concluded with his announcement that he hadn't, after all, been able to find a slot for my media studies course next year.

Sometimes I feel like giving up.

Thursday

A hectic day of last minute preparations for the health food tuck-shop. The sixth year accompanied me in the school minibus to the cash-and-carry, whence we departed with plentiful supply of raisins, apples and nuts. It was tremendously rewarding to see the enthusiasm of these underachievers when presented with a task appropriate to their abilities, and even Sinnot, having been placed in charge of the shopping trolley, launched himself into the project with gusto.

The only absentee from our little excursion was Rose McShane, who declared herself unwilling to join the venture, considering the school meals 'dead gallus' as they were. Having been informed by the art department that the girl has a minor aptitude for artistic design, I offered her the chance to remain in school and devise a painted headboard for my stall, a commission she grudgingly accepted. I told her I wanted something which would attract as much attention as possible. She promised to do her best.

Friday

A calamitous day.

Eager to accord as much responsibility to the sixth-year as possible, and having a class immediately prior to lunch, I had little time to give personal attention to the setting up of the new tuck-shop. Sinnot and Rose McShane, however, promised to take charge and so it was that I found myself hurriedly installed behind the counter at 12 noon with little time to check their preparations.

All seemed to go well at first, and I took a deal of pride in my new proprietorial rôle, clad appropriately in white coat and striped apron. Much hilarity was in evidence from the large gathering of pupils, but I took it to be the usual consequence of seeing something new, and paid little attention. Before long, however, a phalanx of cheering adolescents had gathered round the stall and were evidently enjoying a tremendous private joke between themselves. Following the direction of their creased gazes, I leaned forward to examine the sign which young Miss McShane had so painstakingly designed, painted, and hammered into position above my head: it was difficult to read upside down, but I finally managed to ascertain its import, and immediately recognised the source of everyone's mirth.

'MR SIMPSON'S NUTS . . .' proclaimed the hoarding. My initial reaction was to assume that the poor girl had been unable to see the unfortunate ambiguity so obvious to my potential customers; however, a swift glance in her braying direction gave assurance that my intense embarrassment was almost certainly her sole intention.

Deciding to put a stop to such an undignified scene, I clambered on to the counter in an endeavour to remove the offending sign forthwith. In the meantime, young Sinnot decided upon a demonstration of entrepreneurial flair – if not business acumen – by initiating the random distribution of 'free samples' to his assembled cronies.

'Sinnot!' I bellowed. 'Leave those peanuts alone!'

The boy pretended not to hear and I had little choice other than to forcibly restrain him; unfortunately, I overstretched and sent the entire tuck-shop and its assembled stock cascading across the floor.

It will require little imagination to picture the subsequent scenes of chaos. Suffice to say that a pitched battle ensued, with my entire stock of apples, nuts and raisins providing a veritable feast of ammunition. This being Friday, most of the staff were down at The Pig and Whistle for a pub lunch, and it was only by good fortune that Mr Tod chanced upon the scene and was able to restore order.

He didn't seem very pleased, and at 4 o'clock he took the opportunity to detail his displeasure more fully. In addition to cancelling my entire Enterprise Skills programme, he took the opportunity to announce that he was 'calling in his debts'.

'I don't understand, Mr Tod.'

'The money for your stock, Simpson. We'll need it back, won't we?'

'But that was a grant for start-up costs.'

'It was a *loan*, Mr Simpson. And it's due to be repaid at your earliest convenience.'

I made vehement protest about my inability to pay such a sum, but no argument could prevail; to my further horror, Tod announced that he would therefore have to explore yet another reallocation of requisition sums, and that the English department would find itself even shorter of cash than at the beginning of the week.

I thought carefully. 'A final request, Mr Tod?'

'Yes, Simpson?'

'Please don't tell Miss Bowman before I've got out of the building . . .'

Pickup was just leaving, but I managed to catch him in time. We repaired to The Pig and Whistle and, not for the first time this year, stayed until closing time.

April

The spring term brings, for most teachers, a degree of relief from their everyday teaching duties. Senior classes will normally be excused attendance at school for a period of up to three weeks, which absence enables them to catch up on private revision for their SCE examinations. It allows, also, those teachers whose senior classes are absent the chance to catch up on a variety of developmental tasks: these can range from devising more entertaining lessons for their (still present) junior classes, to tidying up their cupboards or even – in the less enthusiastic backwaters of the educational service – bringing in a few boardgames for some staffroom fun.

Morris, with a timetable almost entirely composed of junior classes, was of course unable to take advantage of such occasions.

Nor, indeed, was his head of department: Angela Bowman had still to arrive at a satisfactory solution with regard to her departmental requisitions. Morris's actions over the preceding two months had

54

obviously made matters worse, but the sums available even before that had been, to Miss Bowman's mind, appallingly low. How she could be expected to run a department on the pittance she was given each spring was really getting beyond her.

Ironically, it was out of such adversity that Morris Simpson's finest hour arose. He owed much gratitude, it must be admitted, to David Pickup, but it was Morris who shone in Miss Bowman's eyes by pointing out that there was, indeed, a good deal of funding available in the world of education: it was just a question of knowing where to look, as his diary entry for April will amply illustrate.

Monday

Departmental acrimony still ensues over Miss Bowman's slashed requisitions. I continue to be held responsible by my head of department for her 60 per cent funding reduction due to the publisher's legal action against the school and my ill-fated attempts to remedy the situation by initiating a health food tuck-shop last month. In a surprising display of immaturity, the wretched woman has made a point of refusing to engage me in any kind of conversation for the last three weeks, and I begin to despair of her forthcoming report to the headmaster on my probationary prospects.

My mood was further depressed this afternoon by the pathetic attitude of my sixth year O grade repeat class, only three of whom bothered to turn up for their last minute pep talk before tomorrow's exam. It was doubly infuriating because I would otherwise have been free of teaching commitments this afternoon; I had, however, recalled the class from their euphemistically entitled 'study leave', and had even absented myself from the annual teachers' Scrabble championship which Mr Major organises during the SCE exam period.

To my extreme annoyance, it further transpired that two of the three were only present because of their misapprehension that the O grade was today, while the third (Rose McShane) had only put in an appearance lest she miss her dinner and the concomitant opportunity to devour three chip butties in the school dining-room.

Such apathy apart, I tried to stress the importance of this, very likely their last chance of attaining an O grade in English. To my surprise, Rose seemed quite overcome with the seriousness of it all and has promised to try and read a poem in preparation. I suggested she stretch herself to finish our class reader, but she refuses to be

55

labelled a swot. I contented myself with a few exhortatory words and a final reminder to turn up in good time for the exam tomorrow.

Tuesday

Some worrying moments of anticipation over the potential contents of the O grade exam. Happily, one of the invigilators smuggled an illicit copy to me some time before the end of the morning and I was relieved to see a goodly selection of the composition topics I'd already practised with my class.

Lunchtime was spent in conversation with Mr Pickup, but we were rudely interrupted by the distraught figure of Rose McShane, who appeared at the staffroom door demanding admittance and the chance to engage 'Mistur Sumpson' in conversation. I hurried to the door.

'Well, Rose, how did it go? What composition topic did you choose, eh?'

'Aw, surr, ah didny!' she bewailed.

'You didn't choose a composition topic? But that's more than half the marks in that part of the –'

'Naw, naw, surr. Ah didny dae anythin' –'

'Didn't do anything? You mean you just sat there twiddling your thumbs?'

'Naw, naw,' she wept. 'Ah slept in, surr. Ah'm just in the now. Kin ah no sit it, surr? Kin ah –'

'Slept in? But what on earth –'

'It wis the telly, surr, it wis a hoarrur fillum an ah jist kidny stoap –'

'A film? On the evening before your O grade exam, when you should have been studying?'

'But ah *did* all ma studyin', surr – right up till midnight, hoanest,' she beseeched me. 'An' then the fillum started aftur that an' ah didny get ma kip till hauf three . . .'

The girl seemed most distressed. Unfortunately, all-night broadcasting appears to allow her limitless opportunities to spend most of her sleeping hours in front of a television screen, hence her frequently distracted expression in class. Indeed, I *had* noticed her increased tendency to snatch forty winks during the course of my lessons, but had merely put it down to an awkward stage in her growing process.

I interrupted her bleatings to explain that I could do nothing further to assist and turned to relate the whole ridiculous affair to

Pickup. As I re-entered the staffroom, Rose's querulous plea sounded faintly behind the door:

'Kin ah no appeal, surr? Kin ah no appeal . . . ?'

Wednesday

A tricky interview with Rose McShane and her parents over the unlikelihood of a successful appeal for the girl's O grade English. Mr McShane, in particular, needed to be forcefully reminded that, given his daughter's appalling academic record, there was no chance whatsoever of her being granted a 'complimentary O level', as he persisted in calling it. I told him that the correct term was a 'compensatory O grade' and that a 'complimentary O level' was an English award which was given away for nothing, but I don't think he understood the difference, or the joke.

The only positive factor to emerge from our interview was the improbable news that Rose has managed to get a job (through a friend of her uncle's . . .) and that I am unlikely to see her again.

I wished her luck and bade farewell, but she has promised to come back for sports day next month and the staff-pupil hockey match at the end of term. I urged her not to bother, but she seemed very keen.

In point of fact, nobody's very sure *what's* going to happen at sports day this year. Miss Honeypot of the PE department has refused to compromise the new found egalitarian principles of physical education and has declared a willingness to organise sports day on the sole condition that all events be labelled non-competitive.

'The kids should be able to enjoy sports day without the threat of being branded as winners and losers,' she claimed at a staff meeting this afternoon. 'We don't *have* winners and losers in PE these days,' she elaborated. 'We just have *participants*.'

The headmaster looked rather bemused by it all, but has nevertheless issued parental invitations for the tea tent. He also asked for staff supervision at various events and has put my name down for the high jump. Mr Pickup says he has a rather old fashioned sense of humour.

Thursday

Sadly, I still find myself ostracised by Miss Bowman, but Mr Pickup presented a novel solution this afternoon during our 4 o'clock pint.

'So Angie Bowman's a bit short of requisition cash, then?'

I confirmed the deficit and explained my own part in the tragedy. 'Why don't you try TVEI, old son?'

Recalling my ill-fated liaison with Harry McSween on last month's Enterprise Skills project, I indicated uncertainty, but – having ordered a second pint and a 'chaser' – Pickup unfolded a machiavellian scheme to equalise the requisition sum available to the English department and reinstate me in Miss Bowman's favour. It all sounded very suspicious, but Pickup persuaded me to give it a try tomorrow morning.

What have I got to lose?

Friday

Pickup's suggestion has been more successful than I'd dared hope!

Having edged my nose around Miss Bowman's door during a free period this morning, I was initially distressed to observe a fearsome accumulation of paperwork on her desk, mainly comprising long columns of addition, subtraction and scored-out lists of textbook requisitions. Miss Bowman herself was angrily jabbing a finger over a pocket calculator as I coughed nervously across the room:

'Oh,' she frowned. 'It's you. What do you want?'

'Time for a quick word, Angela?'

'No, Mr Simpson,' – she emphasised the 'Mister' – 'as you can see, I've got a rather interesting mathematical equation to solve. And it's already –'

'Well, actually,' I interrupted, 'that's what I came about. I know we're a bit short of money in the department, and I know that it's partly my fault –' Miss Bowman drew a sharp breath, but I continued,

'– so I wondered if you'd thought about TVEI?'

'TVEI?' she snapped. 'What about TVEI? I've got enough to worry about running a bankrupt department without getting involved in a half-baked scheme for degenerate teenagers who –'

I rose in Harry McSween's defence: 'Well, actually, Angela, there's a little more to it than that.'

'Oh?'

'Yes. The TVEI scheme is a laudable attempt to drag our school curriculum into the twentieth century. It's providing youngsters with an unrivalled opportunity to develop skills which will be relevant to their employment needs and their leisure interests. It's –'

Miss Bowman snorted, so I called a halt, but added quietly: '– and they've got plenty of money . . .'

She stopped scoffing as the slow dawn of comprehension crossed her troubled brow. Patiently, I explained Mr Pickup's plan (claiming it as my own, of course) to put her 60 per cent shortfall through on Mr McSween's TVEI budget: 'They're rolling in cash, Angela, but there's nothing to spend it on. Tell them you need these books,' I picked out a deleted item from her list, 'to initiate a vocational English course for the fourth year. And tell them you need these,' I highlighted another set of abandoned textbooks, 'to begin an interdepartmental resource base for youngsters going on work experience.'

'But that's a first year poetry anthology, Morris.'

'Doesn't matter. Nobody'll ever look at them. If anyone questions you, tell them the TRIST officer recommended the purchase. That should shut them up.'

For the first time in weeks, Miss Bowman laughed. 'Wonderful! But what about the stationery requisition? I'm still short of 40 reams of foolscap and 500 ballpoints.'

'No problem. Just bung it through on TVEI and say it's for a teenage literacy project. Paper and pens are the first requirement for a teenage literacy project, I'd say . . .'

'Morris,' Miss Bowman smiled. 'You're a genius!' So saying, she took my head between her hands, kissed my forehead, and scurried in the direction of Harry McSween's TVEI rooms.

It was with no small measure of delight that, two hours later, I saw her emerge triumphant and raise both thumbs in my direction. Good old Pickup.

Who says there's no money in education?

May

WEEF

The last months of a school session are traditionally those times when the less academic pursuits are given greater prominence. Sports days and school concerts have for long been an essential part of the June school calendar, but even in these areas of educational provision Morris could discern change and, to his mind, decay.

He had tried, for example, to understand Miss Honeypot's reasoning behind the new approach to competitive sport, but could not find it in his heart to agree: for some pupils, sporting prowess was the only area of school life in which they *could* attain distinction, and it seemed a pity to rob them of what might be their only hour of glory. Rose McShane, it transpired, was an (unlikely) case in point.

The summer term, too, had always been the focal point of many schools' artistic and extra-curricular activities. For those of a musical bent, a school concert would provide the chance of transitory stardom, while others may have had the chance to relax with teachers during an 'activities week', where social, informal contact between staff and pupil would be more important than lessons and learning.

More and more schools, however, had begun to view such pursuits as outwith the legalistic requirements of teachers' duties; additionally, it has to be admitted that a good deal of academic time was lost by such arrangements. Consequently, Parkland High had joined the growing band of schools which started their new sessions in May or June each year, rather than waiting until August. Lessons could begin in earnest, and new SCE courses embarked upon for four vital weeks before the summer holidays began.

Unfortunately, it was all news to Morris. He was still bathing in the reflected glory of David Pickup's innovative solution to the English department's financial problems . . .

Monday

Departmental relations continue to be clothed in harmony since I solved Miss Bowman's requisition problems last month, having nudged her gently in the direction of Harry McSween's TVEI budget. The pot of gold she apparently located therein has done much to supplement the English department's meagre financial allocation. Miss B. has even promised a good probationary report to the headmaster, and I live in hope that I might gain full certification by the end of session.

Bewilderment and confusion, however, arose over new timetable arrangements this morning. To explain: Mr Tod has recently initiated a changeover to next session's timetable during the last weeks of this term. He claims that it allows pupils the chance to get started on their new courses sooner and avoids the appalling waste of time spent on 'freebie jaunts and creaky concerts', as he persists in describing those extra-curricular initiatives which have traditionally contributed to the wider aspects of our summer curriculum.

Speaking as a teacher with more than his fair share of first year classes, my own pleasure in the arrangements can be easily understood: at a stroke, I have lost over one third of my teaching timetable as my youngest charges advance to their second year of comprehensive education; nevertheless, it was some hours this morning before I came to such a full appreciation of the new régime.

There was obviously a breakdown in communication, because news of the changeover had not reached me by the time I prepared to embark upon my first lesson of the day, and I consequently spent some thirty minutes awaiting the arrival of Class 1F without reward. However, having persuaded myself of a vague recollection that Miss

Honeypot had asked for their assistance with Sports Day preparations, I dismissed the matter from my mind.

My uncertainty was nevertheless extended by the arrival of Class 2B for the conclusion of their animal welfare project. In retrospect, I have to admit that a goodly number of the class seemed unfamiliar at the time, and it did strike me as odd that not one of them had the slightest recollection of what page we had reached in the topic-related reader; it was a source of some subsequent annoyance, I must admit, that none of them saw fit to alert me to the fact that they were a new class, freshly promoted from first year, and that this was in fact my first meeting with them. Had they done so, I might have avoided an embarrassing discussion with our depute head after I sought him out during Period 3 to complain about the non-arrival of yet another first year class.

Mr Tod told me, in no uncertain terms and a great deal of eloquent detail, exactly how many times his news of the altered timetable had been posted in the staff bulletin in recent weeks and asked why I hadn't found time to read it. My protestations about pressure of work brought forth the usual response, devoid of any sympathy whatsoever.

'Listen, Simpson: we've *all* got a lot of work to do,' he barked. Sensibly, I refrained from mentioning that *he* certainly gets paid a considerably higher salary for what many of us regard as a timetabling sinecure far removed from the everyday pressures of classroom reality. He continued his tirade: 'And you might be Angie Bowman's blue-eyed boy at present, but you're certainly not mine. If you're wanting me to put in a good word over your probationary report, you'd better pull your socks up – and start reading your ruddy bulletin!'

Tuesday

Preparations for Sports Day tomorrow continue apace; however, Miss Honeypot's insistence that the emphasis be on participation rather than competition remains a source of bewilderment to many of the staff.

'What I can't understand,' queried Mr Pringle at morning break, 'is why the damned woman refuses to award prizes for *anything*. I can see that a sack race is all about a bit of fun, but some of these kids train hard for the proper races: it seems a bit much to expect –'

I broke in to explain the position as explained to me by the PE department last week:

'It's all about equality, Mr Pringle.'

'Eh? What did y'say?' Mr Pringle's increasing deafness and impending retirement have left him a little removed from modern educational thinking, so, at the top of my voice, I attempted to condense Miss Honeypot's arguments:

'They reckon it's unfair,' I shouted across the table, 'for any of the children to be branded as losers, so they simply organise events for the fun of participating, and award certificates to all in recognition of their having taken part. That way, everyone gets the chance to –'

'Balls!' blasted Mr Pickup from the doorway. I was about to take him to task over such an unwholesome intrusion, but it transpired to be an interjection of enquiry rather than exclamation. He has been placed in charge of the fourth year's sponsored netball bounce in aid of Comic Relief (another of Miss Honeypot's alternative activities for sports day) and has, to date, only located four of the necessary thirty six netballs.

Mr Pringle, however, seemed to misinterpret the remark as well: he thrust his pipe firmly betwen clenched teeth, lay back in his armchair, and nodded an agreement in Pickup's direction which brooked no further discussion on the matter. Maybe he's right.

Wednesday

Another day of confusion, most especially for those parents who had turned up at the playing fields in anticipation of some sporting excitement.

The PE department's strictures regarding competition and their refusal to countenance prizes of any sort led to a saddening lack of enthusiasm among those pupils who had bothered to turn up for the occasion. Indeed, the most enlivening part of the day turned out to be Mr Pickup's attempts to resolve an argument which involved 36 girls and 21 netballs.

The senior boys' 100 metres race provided some light relief as well: in a thinly disguised demonstration of disapproval aimed at the new ethos behind sports day, ten participants joined hands at the starting gun and laughingly breasted the tape in unison some nineteen seconds later. Alarmingly enough, Miss Honeypot failed to appreciate the sarcasm and instead viewed their action as a glowing testament to universal brotherhood.

The saddest sight of the afternoon, however, was a disconsolate Rose McShane, returned to school for one day only for the specific purpose of competing in sports day. Her enormous frame was obviously unsuited to all but the most ungainly of pursuits, and she did have something of a task to get into a sack in the first place. Once ensconced, however, and making full use of her wildly flailing elbows, she made an impressive job of outjumping her nine opponents to cross the winning post and emerge triumphant.

Arms aloft, she presented herself at the prize-table, only to be presented with a certificate which proclaimed that she, Rose McShane, had taken part in the 50 metre sack race and had performed to a satisfactory standard.

'Surr? Is that a' that ah get?' she wailed at me in the tea-tent.

'I'm afraid so, Rose,' I confessed.

'That's crap!' she shouted across a gathering of shocked parents. 'Ah've bin comin tae school fur six yeers, an ah've nivir passed an exam, ah've nivir goat a good report, an ah've nivir wun nuthin' – 'cept this race,' she added tearfully. 'It's the only thing ah've ever wun – an you tell me ah dinny get a prize. It's no' ferr!'

Such, I'm afraid, is the logical outcome of physical education's brave new egalitarian world. I confess to a certain sympathy for the girl.

Thursday

Mindful of Mr Tod's injunction about keeping up-to-date with school news, I noticed that the larger part of today's staff bulletin was devoted to the dangers of solvent abuse. One or two of the junior pupils have been indulging in this most dangerous of pastimes, and the headmaster has urged all staff to be on the lookout for the warning signs.

Some empty crisp packets and an assortment of glue-sticks and pots have been discovered behind the old bicycle sheds, so I have paid particular attention to the headmaster's request for extra vigilance in classroom hours.

Friday

A frightful disturbance with my new second-year class this morning, a disturbance specifically related to the headmaster's concern in yesterday's bulletin. With hindsight, I wish I'd never read the damned thing at all . . .

Having spent the first twenty minutes of the period arranging the classroom seating – I always think it's better to let a new class know who's the boss – I had just initiated a group session of improvised role-play situations when one of the more obstreperous pupils called out:

'Haw! Surr! Goanny come here? Jinky's oan the gloo!'

Lunging in the direction of the group concerned, I was horrified to discover James McPhail crouched beneath the lid of his desk, apparently inhaling the last remnants of a particularly pungent glue-stick, surrounded by a band of smirking cronies.

'McPhail!' I bellowed. 'Take that disgusting article away from your face and come with me. At once.'

'But sir,' he gasped, red-eyed and in obvious discomfort, 'I've got –'

That's enough. Just pull yourself together and follow me, please.'

Admitting no sympathy for his distressed state as he struggled to follow in my wake, I frog-marched the boy in Mr Tod's direction.

'And it's no use trying that breathless routine, sonny: you should have thought of that before you got involved in your sniffing exploits. If it was up to me, I'd have the lot of you expelled – but we'll leave that to Mr Tod.'

Dramatically, I knocked on the depute's door and, having gained admission, informed Mr Tod that I had captured one of the ring-leaders in the glue-sniffing brigade. Pausing briefly for the import of my message to sink in, I left young McPhail gazing tearfully across the study and returned to hut A57, confident of future congratulation from the Board of Management.

Mr Tod returned sooner than I had expected and, to my surprise, reintroduced McPhail to the body of the classroom before asking for a quiet word outside.

From bitter experience, I knew the man to be at his most dangerous when asking for a 'quiet word outside': the quieter he tends to be, the more vitrioloic his aggression, and this was no exception.

'Mr Simpson,' he started with ominous calm: 'I'd like to be the first to congratulate you on such a diligent approach to the headmaster's request in yesterday's staff bulletin.'

Uncertain of his mood, but sensing heavy irony, I muttered a non-committal response before he continued, 'though perhaps – if it's not too much trouble – you could *also* find time to read the medical folder which you were given at the start of term.'

'Medical folder, Mr Tod?'

'Yes, medical folder, Mr Simpson.' His mood, as so often before, hardened perceptibly. 'It's bright bloody orange and, if memory serves me right, is sitting on the top shelf of your bookcase in there,' – he motioned towards my classroom – 'most probably unopened since the day you got it last August. Had you investigated its contents before today, you might have remembered that James McPhail is a severe asthmatic.'

'An asthmatic, Mr Tod?'

'Yes, an asthmatic, Mr Simpson. And one who has to have frequent recourse to his inhaler.'

'His inhaler, Mr Tod?'

'Yes, his – good God, man, will you stop repeating everything I say? Yes – his inhaler. He needs it to ward off asthma attacks: unfortunately, he didn't get the full benefit of it today due to the seventy-yard route march you imposed after dragging him from the classroom.'

'But I never imagined for a minute, Mr Tod –'

'Oh, shut up, Simpson. That's just your trouble, isn't it? You never *do* think. Do you really lead your entire life with your head in a bucket of sand?'

It was a ridiculous suggestion, and I refuted the charge at once, but my argument fell upon empty space: Mr Tod had shaken his head, turned on an angry heel, and returned to his study. What chance my probationary report now, I wonder?

June

WEEF

June. The final week of term.

For Mr Pringle, Morris's departmental colleague, it meant the end of a long and increasingly wearisome teaching career. His retirement presentation was to be made at Tuesday's morning break.

For other members of staff, it meant the challenge and excitement of the annual staff-pupil hockey match, normally held on the penultimate day of term. The event, of course, held little practical attraction for Morris, but he planned to wander along and cheer on his colleagues.

It is a week of mixed emotions, this final week of term: for many teachers, there is a tinge of sadness as they watch their young charges depart for the adult world; for others, it is a time of blessed relief as they rid themselves of some particularly troublesome pupil for good. The very phrase, 'final week of term', tends to bring to a teacher's mind so many memories, so many nuances: it can evoke the smell of new-mown grass outside the classroom window, or perhaps the chance to pick up chairs and conduct lessons in the playground, under a warm and welcoming sun; it can evoke recollections of quiet, hopeful farewells, or of classes with pupil-teacher ratios at their lowest level of the year, as more and more youngsters take the opportunity to break up early; it can evoke the pleasant thoughts of staff outings, all *bonhomie* and cheerfulness, and it can evoke the restful, delicious chance to contemplate the six long weeks of escape which lie ahead.

Also, of course, the final week of term can evoke memories of Wimbledon, and the age-old staff tradition of nipping into the school TV rooom to catch up on the latest news from the courts. Sadly, Parkland High was not immune from such tennis fever, and even members of the senior management team found themselves occasionally athirst for a progress report on the latest mixed-doubles tie.

For Morris, of course, the last week of term meant only one thing. Would he get his parchment?

Monday

I am still concerned about my final probationary report, and can only hope that the board of management which claims to run Parkland High will give sympathetic consideration to the behavioural difficulties I've encountered in certain of my pupils. In point of fact, Miss Bowman has given the headmaster a very favourable report of my departmental contributions, and has recommended that I be granted full registration with the GTC. I would like to think that such an attitudinal shift on her part owes much to my dedicated efforts in the classroom, but suspect that I made a deeper impression with the suggestion that she supplement departmental funds with a large cash injection from the TVEI budget. The department has never been better equipped . . .

The headmaster himself seems to regard my possible certification with a degree of equanimity, having no doubt been impressed with my carefully timed offer to restart extra-curricular activities next session, in the shape of a junior chess club.

Unfortunately, I have yet to convince Mr Tod, our depute head, that I am fit to be granted the glowing testimonial I so desire and, although the writing of my final report rests with Mr Ross, Mr Tod has a great deal of influence. I have tried to make myself acceptable in his sight but to little effect: his observation that my proposed chess club was merely a 'last crawling lunge' struck me as symptomatic of the man's vindictive and spiteful approach to me since the day I embarked upon a teaching career.

On a lighter note, I have politely refused the sixth year's request that I take part in their staff-pupil hockey match on Thursday.

Such informal meetings between masters and children do little to contribute to professional dignity.

Tuesday

Mr Pringle's retirement presentation took place at afternoon break, attended by those members of staff who managed to drag themselves from the television room and its attendant coverage of the Wimbledon tennis fortnight. Mr Pringle, having taught for thirty-four years (the last thirty in Parkland High) has opted for early retirement. His loss will not be felt, to be honest, for he was never in the forefront of educational reform, and had only recently discovered the availability of the Banda machine as a means of duplicating classroom material.

Nevertheless, I found his speech of acceptance somewhat depressing in tone, for he seemed to suggest that he was only too glad to escape what he termed the 'unceasing hostilities of the classroom and the increasing administrative burden of everyday teaching'. Furthermore, he claimed that the abolition of corporal punishment had been 'the worst event in the history of Scottish education' – an observation for which he was warmly applauded, believe it or not!

I shook my head in silent disapproval, and was further horrified when Pickup explained that the wretched man wasn't actually retiring until August, on the first day of next session.

'Well,' I queried him after the interval: 'why can't he get his presentation in August, then?'

'Because he'll be sick, I imagine.'

'Why? Is he retiring on health grounds?'

'Other than mental anguish, not that I know of. No: he's not retiring until August 18th so that he gets paid for the holidays. But I don't expect we'll see him back inside the front door after the end of June – he's probably handed in his sick line for August already.'

'You mean he's actually organised his retirement date so that he gets paid for six weeks of doing nothing?'

'Of course. Everybody else does.'

I found it hard to believe, but Pickup seemed certain of his facts. I told him such an action was morally reprehensible and against all principles of honesty, but he told me to wait thirty-five years and see where my principles were then.

It's all very sad.

Wednesday

A satisfying day, in the course of whioh any doubts about my
probationary report have been cleared away.

To explain, I chanced to cross the headmaster's extremely agitated
path just after lunchtime. He demanded to know the wherabouts of
'that bloody Tod', and explained that a matter of the utmost urgency
had arisen for which he required the instant services of his depute.

I was just about to volunteer the information he so peremptorily
requested, when thoughts of discretion crossed my mind.

'I – um – think he's with the – ah – 4th year careers guidance,' I
lied smoothly, before making a tentative offer to fetch him which
gained immediate acceptance.

'And be quick about it!' Mr Ross bellowed after me. 'It's urgent!'

A swift dash to the staffroom noticeboard confirmed my suspicions:
the television room had ben set aside under Mr Tod's name for
the entire afternoon under the somewhat nebulous description of
'Vocational Leisure Course'. Knowing full well that we possess no
such course, I nipped upstairs to discover the depute head and a
goodly collection of staff engrossed in a thrilling singles match from
Wimbledon, having apparently abdicated all professorial responsibility.

I sidled up to Tod and whispered the headmaster's message in his
ear, whereupon he jumped like a scalded cat and scurried downstairs.

I still haven't discovered what was so important about it all, but
am only pleased to report that Tod made the effort to seek me out
at four o'clock and thank me for not – as he put it – 'blowing his
cover'.

'Yes, Simpson,' he continued. 'You showed great presence of
mind today. And great resourcefulness. Just the kind of qualities,'
he added somewhat grudgingly, 'that we need in today's young
teachers.'

I smiled weakly, as he concluded his speech of gratitude: 'And
that's exactly what I was saying to Mr Ross this afternoon. I think
you should find he's more than willing to recommend your full
registration with the GTC – at last.'

I started to offer profuse thanks, but Mr Tod prevented me:

'Don't mention it, Morris. One good turn, as they say. Just enjoy
the last few days of term, and then go and have a good holiday.
We've got a busy session ahead!'

Revenge is sweet.

Thursday

Despite my unwillingness to be associated with the hockey match in any active capacity, I nevertheless felt beholden to lend some support as an interested spectator, particularly in view of the fact that Rose McShane was making her final appearance as a pupil of Parkland High School. Despite the manifold problems of discipline with which she's presented me over the past twelve months, I confess to a soft spot for the wretched girl: a young woman of such enormous girth, not to mention her severe behavioural problems and profoundly limited intelligence, is not going to find life easy in the outside world, and I looked forward to seeing how she acquitted herself on the playing fields.

Having taken my place on the touchline at 4pm, it was with some amusement that I viewed the motley collection which made up the teachers' side. Mr Pickup, in particular, looked a ridiculous figure, his rapidly enlarging beer gut hanging over a pair of ridiculously tight shorts, themselves clinging obscenely to a pair of 15 denier black tights he had borrowed specially for the occasion. The organisational incapabilities of the staff side were highlighted by the fact that they discovered themselves without a goalkeeper some three minutes – and one goal – after the game's commencement.

Their consequent demands for my presence on the field of play were not long in coming, and my protestations of inexperience were to no avail.

'Oh, just stand in the goal, Morris!' boomed Pickup. 'Take off your jacket and bung on a couple of pads. We won't let them near you again!'

Loath to spoil the end-of-term atmosphere, I shuffled round to the staff goal and was in the process of removing my sports jacket when goal number two whizzed past my ear. Increasingly dubious about Pickup's reassurances, I had just concluded padding up when the terrifying vision of Rose McShane in gym-slip – bearing close resemblance to a ship in full and awesome sail – came bearing down upon me. Hockey stick aloft, she was at the forefront of a fearsome herd of viragoes, her throat rasping with a shrieking, petrifying war-cry – 'HEER WE GOA! HEER WE GOA! HEER WE GOA! CHAAARRGE!' It was the last thing I remember hearing.

Pickup told me afterwards that I'd stood up really well to the first collision, but that the combined weight of Rose McShane and Karen Sloss had been too much for my relatively slender frame and that, for a brief interval before the arrival of an ambulance, my potential survival had been in question, given that the first eleven in its entirety had seemed to bury me from sight.

'Still,' he chortled during hospital visiting-time, 'could've been a nice way to go, old son: buried under a heap of writhing teenage flesh. Almost envied you for a minute.'

I snorted, winced, and reminded Pickup that it was impossible to laugh with two broken ribs and a leg in traction, even had I felt like it. As it was, I had the prospect of several days in hospital and a completely ruined summer holiday, all due to his ruddy hockey match.

He seemed surprised that I didn't want to know the final score.

Friday

A touching deputation from school on this, the last day of term. Despite the ward sister's instructions concerning 'two visitors to a patient', Mr Ross and the senior Board of Management gathered round my bedside at afternoon visiting time for the specific purpose of presenting my final probationary report.

Glowing with satisfaction, I listened as the headmaster read me a set of comments which, if not exactly fulsome in their praise, nevertheless confirmed that, after three years of probation, he at last recommended that I be granted full registration with the General Teaching Council.

Having awkwardly appended my signature from a horizontal position, I passed the document back.

'There,' said Mr Ross. 'Now you're a fully certified teacher at last . . .'

I think he failed to see the irony.

Pickup, lurking in the background, scoffed a comment to the effect that such registration was unlikely to do me any good:

'The only time you'll hear from those buggers at the GTC will be when they dock five quid off your salary each year, Simpson. If I were you, I'd resign before you join!'

I chided him sharply for such continued lack of professionalism, but he mellowed somewhat once the senior members of staff had disappeared:

'And here's a little something,' he whispered over my upraised leg, 'to while away the lonely hours.' So saying, he surreptitiously slipped a six-pack of special-brew lager under the bedclothes before revealing latest news from the school.

'You remember,' he confided, 'old Ross getting his knickers in a twist last Wednesday and sending for Deputy Dog?'

I nodded assent, and raised an eyebrow of enquiry.

'It's big trouble,' he continued. 'Big trouble.'

I waited for elaboration.

'The Area Review Group,' Pickup whispered dramatically. 'They're coming to Parkland next session.'

Initially unaware of the import behind the revelation, Pickup soon acquainted me with the problem of falling rolls in all of our town's schools, and the consequences for the forthcoming session.

'We've got a battle on our hands, Simpson, and no mistake. Just make sure you're fit and well come August 18th.'

Unable to contemplate the rigours of what Pickup expects to be a bloody combat to save the school, I gazed into the middle distance. Suddenly astonished, my eyes alighted on a beaming figure ambling up the ward, a bunch of ragged carnations wrapped in yesterday's newspaper and clutched in a cumbersome and soil-encrusted hand. Rose McShane, no less!

'Surr!' she bawled, grabbing an empty sample bottle which she apparently mistook for a vase, and thrusting her gift firmly into its neck. 'Ah jist had tae cum an' see ye. Urr ye a'right, surr? Urr ye?'

I nodded a weak smile of assent, as Rose handed me a self-produced card of condolence. 'GETT WEL SUNE – OR ELS!' it threatened, along with the touching refrain beneath: 'TO MY FAYVRIT TEE-CHUR – FROM ROSE MCSHANE . . .'

Even Pickup managed a benevolent smile as a tear of gratitude rose to my eye. Teaching has its rewards after all.

August: the New Session

The injuries which Morris had sustained during his heroic stand between the staff goalposts meant that he was unable to enjoy the full benefit of his six-week break from school. Not so Simon Major: as Morris lay in his hospital bed on that last Friday of term, the majority of the staff gathered together for a farewell party: its culmination was Mr Major's donning of last year's holiday sombrero and whistling a tuneless rendition of *Y Viva Espana*, as he celebrated his imminent departure for a continental villa.

But Morris had many matters to occupy his mind during his recuperation period, not least of which was the recently announced threat of school closures. The problem of under-utilised schools had been an enormous regional headache for some months now: how could education authorities claim a shortage of adequate financial funding when, with declining pupil numbers, they were seen to be maintaining half-empty schools which should quite properly be merged?

The proposed closure of a local school, however, can be a difficult political bullet to bite: of course it was right that under-utilised schools should shut their doors, said parents and teachers in unison – as long as it's not *our* school they plan to close down.

In such a situation, it is difficult for a regional authority to be anybody's friend, though in the early days of potential closures Lothian region made an admirable attempt to be *everybody's* by refusing to close or merge *any* school, no matter how pathetic its roll;

Strathclyde, on the other hand, caused a good deal of controversy in trying to bulldoze through its most celebrated closure attempt, that of Paisley Grammar. The political machinations behind this attempt, the subsequent government intervention and equally political rule-change to *prevent* the school's closure, were all recorded in both educational and national press at the time, and at great length. Suffice to say that when a local authority was keen to close a school which suffered from being over 100 per cent *full*, it ill behoved any school to consider its position safe. And for a school such as Parkland High, the writing was likely to be well and truly on the wall.

As the new session dawned, however, Morris tried to cast such worries to the back of his mind and relish, instead, the prospect of his first academic year as a 'proper teacher'. The term was due to start on Tuesday, with two days of in-service provision.

Monday

Having finally received full certification from the GTC, I find myself looking forward with keen anticipation to the forthcoming session. Free at last of my probationer tag, I look forward to receiving a good deal more respect from the pupils under my charge – not to mention my teaching colleagues!

The last week of my summer holidays has been spent in finalising lesson plans for the coming term and today has seen me packing a briefcase ready for tomorrow's fray. Such meticulous preparations seem to be in stark contrast to those embarked upon by Mr Major, our euphemistically entitled assistant headteacher: I understand he flies into the country this evening, having spent the last six weeks in a Spanish self-catering villa.

Sadly, any happiness gained in the eventual granting of my parchment last session has been overshadowed by the news that Parkland High is under threat of closure from the Area Review Group due to be set up this autumn; Mr Pickup, my middle-aged mentor from religious education (and geography), has warned me to apply for a transfer before – to use his inimitable phraseology – 'the shit hits the fan'. I have told him to wait and see; personally, I think it highly unlikely that a school as popular as Parkland High could figure in any closure discussions.

Tuesday

A fresh start to a fresh term, or so it seemed as I entered the school gates this morning. Parkland High had been graced with a new coat of paint during the holidays and it really made the old place look a good deal more presentable. In addition, a new nameplate had been erected outside the front door and even, apparently, a new name: *Parkland Community High School* was the legend emblazoned across the portals as I strolled across the car park, and I made mental note to enquire about our newly found community status as soon as possible.

Once inside, however, renewal of acquaintanceships pushed the matter from my mind, and I soon found myself engrossed in our introductory staff meeting. Actually, 'engrossed' is hardly an accurate description of my attitude, for our first in-service day comprised the usual collection of injunctions concerning a whole host of administrative paraphernalia, all of which seemed a hundred miles removed from the business of teaching. As always, the headmaster issued stern warning to switch off the staffroom tea-urn after use; as always, he will be ignored.

Indeed, the contents of Mr Ross's pre-term pep-talk were entirely indistinguishable from last year's, with the sole exception of an innovatory competition he intends launching on a monthly basis. Bereft of ideas to initiate continuous staff development, I gather that bottles of wine are to be offered in return for suggestions to fill up his planned activity timetable, the outlining of which has caused him no little anxiety during the summer months.

The only other unusual aspect of our morning session was the constant presence of a photographer, who kept up an endless irritation of clicks and scrapes as he wandered the room, snapping at will. I queried Mr Pickup during the staff's midday pub lunch, but he scoffed at my suggestion that the headmaster was looking for illustrative material for the school prospectus.

'No, no,' he laughed, '– though God knows it could do with some tarting up! No, no,' he repeated, 'It's all part of a public relations extravaganza dreamed up by the dynamic duo during the summer hols.'

I passed no comment on his disrespectful reference to Messrs Ross and Tod, our head and depute respectively, but pressed for elaboration on his theme.

'Good grief, Simpson,' he chided. 'Waken up! It's the closures, isn't it?'

Shaking a frustrated head at my vacant expression, he continued: 'If we're under threat of closure, we've got to start mobilising the grand forces of publicity. And who do we get on our side first of all?

The local press. That's what the photographer johnnie was there for this morning. The head's got him running a story called 'Parkland Prepares . . .' or some such God-awful nonsense. After that, he'll have him dragged along to every tuppeny affair we can muster, from sponsored walks to sponsored sleeps, and a couple of garden parties thrown in as well. And after that, he'll reform the PTA –'

'PTA?' I questioned.

'Ah. Before your time, Morris. We used to have a Parent-Teacher Association, in the BTA days.' Swiftly, he anticipated my query: 'Before the Action, old son. And mark my words: he'll have us out there running cake-bakes and musical evenings every spare minute of the day if that's what it takes to convince some half-baked councillor that *his* school is an integral part of the community, while the one down the road is –'

Pickup's mention of the community reminded me of the new nameplate, and I interrupted with further enquiry.

'Exactly!' he triumphed. 'It's a scream, isn't it? The headmaster's idea, of course. He reckons that they wouldn't give a toss about shutting down Parkland High School. But Parkland *Community* High School: well, that's a different matter. So he's had us re-named during the summer holidays, and hopes no-one will notice. Ironic, really,' he mused, 'when you consider we've very little to do with the community – and, if we're honest about it, even less to do with education . . .'

I rebuked Pickup for his cynicism, and suggested a return to work. He bade me farewell and proclaimed an intention to 'stay for a quickie'. Whisky glass in hand, he bade me farewell and warned against accepting a seat on the PTA when the offer came.

Wednesday

Further valuable time spent in pointless meetings over administration. The only information of any value to be gleaned was a form list for my register class, 2F, and the news that one of the guidance staff has become pregnant. There may be a chance of a temporary promoted post if I play my cards right.

Mr Major finally showed up late this morning, after a twenty-seven hour flight delay due to Spanish air-traffic problems. He looked bronzed but weary, and spent the entire afternoon ensconced in his office with the door locked. Mr Pickup commented that nobody had noticed his absence anyway and probably wouldn't have done so for at least six weeks, such was his contribution to the efficient running of the school. I rebuked him again, and informed him that Major had once told me that an assistant headteacher's work was often unseen, but nonetheless valuable for that. Pickup snorted in derision.

Photographer still around.

Thursday

My first meeting with 2F, some of whose members I know from last year. I have decided to keep a fairly tight grip on them, as several of my colleagues have informed me that this is the year 'they start growing horns'; if I'm to get anywhere in Guidance, I want to make sure that my own register class is a model of propriety. I gave them a fairly stiff pep-talk to indicate my demands for firm discipline at all times, but was constantly interrupted by Gordon Lawson's news that the photographer was still in school:

'Surrr! Surr! Ah goat ma fotie took! Did yoo, surr? Did ye? Did ye?'

Before I had time to quell the wretched boy for the fifth time in as many minutes, his claims had elicited thirty shouted revelations of a similar nature from his peers: apparently the headmaster has requested a comprehensive dossier of the numerous activities – both academic and extra-curricular – which contribute to the ethos of Parkland Community High School and looks forward to seeing a fulsome report of our opening days in tomorrow's local paper.

Personally, I was a little offended that he hadn't seen fit to obtain a picture of the Junior Chess Club which I restarted at lunchtime. It seems likely to be a tremendous success: over 45 boys and a handful of girls turned up at 1 o'clock. Things should really take off once we get some chess sets.

Friday

The headmaster's strategy for publicity appears to have backfired with a vengeance. Today's edition of the *Parkland Gazette* has certainly allocated a tremendous amount of column inches to the school's new term, but has sadly sacrificed accuracy for sensationalism.

A ten point banner headline – BACK TO SCHOOL! – framed a disgraceful montage of photographs which numbered, among others, a furtive band of junior pupils congregated in 'smokers' corner', sharing a packet of twenty king-size cigarettes between them.

Another, more lurid picture, featured Gordon Lawson and Amanda Scott locked firmly in passionate embrace.

The accompanying caption – 'Parkland High: under-age smoking, under-age loving – and lunch-time drinking . . .' invited the reader's eyes to further contemplate a picture of the staff's 'so-called in-service provision'. Underneath a photograph which portrayed the large majority of staff entering The Pig and Whistle at lunchtime on Tuesday, a report which owed much to the writer's imagination suggested that 'staff spend more of these extra holidays drinking liquor than devising lessons'. Unfortunately, such ridiculous assertions were given credence by a somewhat unfortunate photograph of Mr Pickup, an inane grin across his face, raising a shaky glass of whisky to the camera's gaze. Why, the reporter asked, was this man still drinking at half past two when the afternoon in-service had started at half past one?

In a distressing example of editorial malevolence, a further report went on to reveal the appalling example set by Mr Major's late arrival for the new term: 'One senior member of the school staff,' it informed its readers, 'found that a six-week holiday was not long enough for his needs. Simon Major, an assistant headteacher at Parkland High, strolled in to work *thirty-six hours late*, having spent the last two months sunning himself on a Spanish topless beach . . .'

The headmaster was furious, and summoned Pickup and Major for immediate high level talks. Unable to refute the photographic evidence on offer, he is nevertheless writing a letter of complaint to the newspaper, asking that they at least accord the school its proper designation as a Community High School. He is unlikely to invite them to any further functions . . .

The only note of happiness for Mr Ross appears to have been the response to his new competition: the prospect of a free bottle of wine has motivated unparalleled educational enthusiasm in the staff, and he has been showered with suggestions for the profitable use of planned activity time.

It is a source of some gratification, then, to report that my own suggestion of greater liaison with our two feeder primary schools has been taken up for next month's topic. Mr Ross seemed to think it a tremendous idea to invite one of the headteachers along to address the staff on primary teaching methods.

'Hah!' guffawed Pickup at afternoon break. 'I'm sure he did! It'll certainly mean he hasn't to do anything himself except book the lecture theatre and then sit back.'

79

I was about to defend the headmaster when Mr Major emerged from behind a newspaper and a screen of pipe tobacco:

'Ah! So it was *your* ruddy idea, Simpson?'

My assent, and further claims for the immense value to be gained from such interdisciplinary liaison, met a withering storm of abuse:

'Listen, sonny: I've been teaching for thirty one years now, and I've spent the last fifteen trying to re-teach all the things they used to learn in primary school. And now you tell me that some jumped up wifie without a proper qualification's going to come and tell *me* how *she* organises her teaching methods – such as they are. I should cocoa!'

For once, Pickup and Major were in complete agreement, and I am left with a degree of apprehension about the welcome they are likely to accord Miss Hatfield at our planned activity session next month. It hardly seems the right attitude.

September

WEEF.

Mr Major's condemnation of the primary sector could hardly be described as reasoned or fair, but his attitude nevertheless reflected a not uncommon sentiment among secondary teachers.

Conditioned by years of a separate salary scale, and lifelong membership of the SSTA (Scottish Secondary Teachers' Association), Mr Major had always viewed work in the secondary school as a *real* teaching job, and the introduction of a single salary scale as part of the 1986 pay settlements had been a tremendous blow – to him and to his union. To Simon Major, primary teaching was little more than a glorified form of child-minding. He had not, of course, been in a primary school since he was twelve.

The EIS (Educational Institute of Scotland), on the other hand, had long made strong claim to the equal worth of *both* sectors: its pre-eminent position in teacher trade-unionism was to a certain extent due to the immense number of primary teachers among its ranks, and it certainly had no objection to these members being paid equal amounts to their secondary colleagues.

However, despite the abolition of one of its main reasons for existence, the SSTA nevertheless remained a presence in Scottish education. There were always teachers – such as Morris Simpson – who saw the EIS as un unhealthy force of militants, hell-bent upon petty trade-unionism rather than the needs of the children under their care. The meeting which David Pickup, EIS representative at Parkland, called on a Monday in September was a case in point. As will be seen, discontent was still rife over in-service provision.

Monday

A joint union meeting to discuss the contentious issue of Planned Activity Time. For the first occasion in living memory, members of our two main teaching unions have agreed to settle their differences and plan alternative strategies in response to the enforced detention being foisted upon them by a remote hierarchy of officialdom. Even my own union – traditionally moderate, if occasionally slightly slow on the uptake – has been moved to protest in measured terms at the waste of time occasioned by the plethora of valueless in-sevice provision.

Mr Pickup, indeed, has made his feelings clear: having taken over as representative of the school's largest union following the early retirement of Mr Pringle last session, he has been particularly incensed at the lack of trust implied in teachers' professionalism, and said as much to me at morning break:

'It's bloody ridiculous, Simpson: they seem intent upon treating us like recalcitrant children instead of responsible adults. Next thing you know, they'll have us clocking in at the school gates every morning. The only way we can beat this thing is by all pulling together and forgetting our differences – so I hope to see you and the rest of the Mothers' Union members at lunch-time – O.K.?'

Sadly, such triumphant expressions of brotherly solidarity and adult responsibility had assumed a bitterly ironic twist by lunchtime, for the eventual meeting comprised an entirely one-sided discussion between members of my own union, Mr Pickup having received instructions from head office between break and midday. The central thrust of a subsequent injunction to his own members was to forbid them discussing PAT until they were in receipt of a more detailed, official policy from the union's strategy unit. So blinkered were his membership in their desire to toe the party line that – following Pickup's initial explanation of their unwillingness to take part in a meeting which *they* had called – not one of them gave utterance throughout the entire forty minutes.

At least it gave *me* a chance to speak for once, and I made it very clear that I thought their attitude to be irresponsible, petulant, and childish in the extreme.

'I can only hope,' I concluded, 'that you accord our visiting primary head a deal more politeness during Planned Activity Time tomorrow. We could all learn a lot from Miss Hatfield, and she won't be very impressed if –'

A sinister, vindictive hissing filled the room, and fifty pairs of eyes looked set to kill. I drew my speech to an uncertain conclusion and sat down.

Tuesday

Further disharmony over PAT and, in particular, the in-service contribution of Miss Hatfield, recently appointed head teacher of Parkland Primary School, and invited to the school at my behest to encourage a greater degree of liaison between Parkland High and its feeder primaries.

Personally, I found her talk both stimulating and informative: she outlined the exciting developmental work being undertaken by our colleagues in the primary sector, and even enlisted the assistance of Mr Tod, our depute, in the performance of a rôle play to demonstrate the benefits of open improvisation and pair-work. In particular, I was most impressed by her explanation of the 'infusion' method of teaching grammar to under-achievers, and she had some fascinating things to tell us about teaching methods for primary maths as well. Apparently, for example, they no longer do subtraction; rather, they go in for 'decomposition', a revelation which drew a rather abusive snort from Mr Dunbar of maths, seated on my left-hand side. Anyway, I found it all jolly interesting.

Sadly, my enthusiasm was not shared by Mr Pickup and his little coterie, all of whom refused to contribute to the session in any shape or form. Somewhat unnerved by their impoliteness, Miss Hatfield made the mistake of becoming slightly over-enthusiastic in her re-commendation of primary methods for the secondary sector:

'In particular,' she urged, 'I can't help saying that you could brighten the place up a bit. Walk into any primary school in the region and you'll see brightly coloured walls laden with attractive displays of the children's work. Come into Parkland High, and the only wall display is crumbling plasterwork and an occasional free poster from the Scottish Health Education Group – usually five years out of date . . . It's really not conducive to a genuine *enjoyment* of education, is it?'

Insensitive to the swelling indignation of her audience, the unfortunate woman floundered deeper:

'And the serried ranks of desks don't help much, either. Why don't you try to give the children more *freedom* occasionally? Of course, it can't be easy without an open plan building, but I think you could make a start somewhere. Perhaps you could prioritise by arranging a –'

It was all too much for Mr Pickup.

'What? Prioritise? What the hell d'you mean, woman?

Miss Hatfield stumbled, flustered: 'Prioritise? Well, it's simply . . . um . . . give yourselves . . . um . . . arrange to give certain matters attention in an order of priority.'

'Then why the hell can't you say that, instead of tarting it up with all that ridiculous jargon you keep spouting?' barked Pickup, in an astonishing display of rudeness. To my horror, he was applauded by a large cross-section of the audience. Even worse, our assistant head, Mr Major, then chose to join in the attack:

'Hear! Hear!' he bellowed. 'If you ask me, dearie,' – the reference made Miss Hatfield flinch, but she stood her ground bravely – 'we could do with a lot less fancy theory and silly games in your precious primary schools, and a damned sight more hard work from the little buggers. In case you didn't know,' he continued, 'we're supposed to get them ready for exams in this place, and it doesn't help matters if we've got to spend the first six months of every year teaching your little toe-rags how to read and write properly!'

Miss Hatfield seemed about to defend herself, but her face, which had grown more astonished with every passing insult from Major, suddenly crumpled into tears, and she made a hasty exit. The headmaster stared angrily at Pickup and seemed about to launch in his direction, but thought better of it and rushed, instead, in the wake of Miss Hatfield to offer tea and consolation.

A sense of triumph across his features, Mr Pickup proposed the motion that such departures signalled the end of PAT for the day. The resolution was passed *nem con.*

Wednesday

A terrible dressing down for Messrs Pickup and Major from the headmaster this morning. He was particularly infuriated that yesterday's incident had overshadowed his efforts to save the school from threatened closure by the introduction of innovatory curricular development, and warned them that repetition of such behaviour would bode ill for the future survival of Parkland Community High (as he still insists on calling us).

Mr Major seemed unperturbed at morning break:

'If you ask me,' he ventured, 'this business of school closures is a damned good thing. Look at the situation. We've got so many surplus places in this town that we could shut down at least two schools entirely, and nobody would be worse off.'

'Were you thinking of Parkland High?' I queried.

'Good God, no,' scoffed Major. 'Shut *us* down? Certainly not. But let's face it: there are one or two schools should be at the top of the list, and I don't need to name them.

'I'll say one thing for this Government,' he continued, warming to his theme: 'this Parents' Charter has certainly given them freedom of choice. It means that a school like ours is bound to remain open for business – and get a bit more cash into the bargain. No, no, sonny,' he wagged an admonitory finger in my direction: 'Parkland High won't be for the chop – and nor will J.P. Major. Our jobs are safe enough, don't you worry.'

I hope he's right.

Thursday

Chess Club day. Enthusiasm for the club has grown enormously, so that I now have sixty-four pupils crammed into Hut A57 at lunch-time – and sometimes double that if it's raining.

Unfortunately, we have still to procure any chess sets, and funding from the headmaster's social fund has not been forthcoming. Andrew Stothers of 1G has brought in a set of draughts, but it's become increasingly difficult to demonstrate the subtleties of a Sicilain defence with such limited facilities. Certain disciplinary problems associated with the club have consequently arisen, and Mr Tod has threatened to close us down. I hope not. My chess club is the only available form of leisure for some of these pupils.

Friday

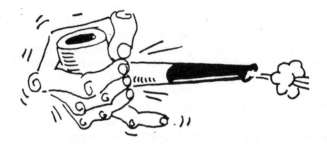

An about-turn by Mr Major on the matter of school closures.

Blissfully assured of the school's future survival, he seems never to have considered the possibility that – even if the school remains intact – there will be other teachers, from other schools, all looking to remain in continued employment. In particular, the potential arrival of four other assistant head teachers at Parkland seems not to have crosed his mind.

It was Mr Pickup, indeed, who drew his atention to an article in this morning's local paper. Provocatively entitled 'Getting Rid of the Dross', it went on to elaborate the thesis that a surplus of promoted teachers in employment across the town would be thinned out by a 'judicious combination of early retirements and re-interviews'.

'What!' spluttered Major, his pipe clenched firmly between a set of very white knuckles. 'Re-interview? They can't do that. They've already appointed us. They can't go back on that. Can they?' he quavered.

''Fraid so,' confirmed Pickup. 'If they've got two AHTs and only one job, then it's an interview situation, old man. But never mind,' he consoled, a malicious grin across his face: 'anyone who's done as

86

much as you have for the school shouldn't need to worry. It's only the time-servers they'll want to kick downstairs . . .'

Major glanced up from his arm-chair, rightly uncertain of Pickup's sincerity. An angry frown upon his face, he launched a vitriolic attack on the government's policy of school closures and its market-place mentality.

'But surely,' I interrupted, 'you were saying exactly the opposite just the other –'

'Shut it, Simpson,' he ordered, and stormed out of the staffroom.

By 4 o'clock, he had written – and issued to every pupil – an open letter to parents inviting them to join the 'Save Our School' campaign. A meeting has been arranged for next month, and Major has appointed himself Chairman.

What a difference a day makes . . .

October

It was perhaps no bad thing that Simon Major had at last found an educational cause for which he thought it worthwhile to mount a struggle, even if it *was* a struggle largely based on self-interest.

The EIS, meanwhile, had launched a campaign on a much broader front concerning the alterations to Scottish education which were being made by a government which, it claimed, had no mandate to effect such reform in Scotland. The executive's decision to call a one day strike in November to draw attention to the 'Anglicisation of Scottish education' was, ultimately, well enough supported by the membership, though members of the public were perhaps uncertain about the reasons behind yet another burst of teachers' industrial action. The government, in the guise of Messrs Rifkind and Forsyth – then Secretary of State and Minister of Education respectively – paid little heed other than to rubbish the EIS for harming the education of innocent children.

One area where the Scottish Office *did* appear to take heed of educational demand, however, was in the realm of modern language teaching. The fact that modern languages had no place in the 'core curriculum' of future Scottish education became, eventually, a source of some embarrassment to a government which had spent a lot of money publicising the growing internationalism and breaking down of continental barriers which would herald the arrival of 1992.

A spectacularly successful campaign of persuasion was launched by Scottish language teachers, who pointed out the anomaly of their country's unique insularity in the subject of foreign language study. The case was eventually won and – staffing implications notwithstanding – the study of a foreign language was declared compulsory, at least up to Standard grade. The implications for Parkland High soon became apparent.

Morris Simpson, unaffected by the languages debate, and untroubled by any moral dilemmas over calls for industrial action, found himself nevertheless concerned about his unattractive timetable. Despite being in his fourth full year of teaching (and his first of full registration), his timetable still comprised the kind of dog's breakfast more normally associated with a new entrant to the profession. The only escape from his standard collection of junior classes had been the introduction of a fifth year Enterprise Skills class: although a difficult group to control, Morris still looked forward to his sessions with them. They were something of a challenge.

It was a challenge which was to prove especially demanding during the last week of October, when his carefully prepared lesson plans were being constantly interrupted by a particularly noisy firm of glaziers.

Monday

I finally appear to be getting through to my Enterprise Skills class. This ill-assorted group of Christmas leavers – allocated to my timetable by Miss Bowman in order to afford some relief from the constant diet of first and second-year pupils – has proved a difficult nut to crack, especially from a disciplinary point of view. This morning, however, I gave them a stiff talk about the benefits to be achieved by displaying initiative and enthusiasm for helping themselves:

'It's no use,' I berated, 'moaning about a lack of opportunity. This country offers *tremendous* opportunity to those who are willing to get up and go for it. Show some initiative – that's what this Enterprise Skills course is designed to get you thinking about – and you'll soon find that there's *something* you can do that provides a decent standard of living. Too many people still expect the state to provide everything for them: what you've got to do is get out there and make it happen for yourselves!'

I think I was making some kind of impression, though it was difficult to make myself heard above the din created by the glazing firm which had arrived to remedy the damage perpetrated by the weekend vandals. Such wanton destruction is becoming completely intolerable: the glaziers are practically taking up permanent residence on Monday mornings to replace innumerable panes of broken glass, and the consequent racket is insufferable.

Gaining the full attention of my class was made no easier by Andrew Greig's constant attempts to lean out of his seat and wave at the foreman of the glaziers; having been reprimanded for the umpteenth time, he at last agreed to return to his seat, but only after proudly informing the class that the said foreman – and owner of the firm – was his own father, and that a job in the family business was his for the asking.

My perfectly reasonable query about the relevance of this information to our discussion was met by a disgracefully framed reply to the effect that he therefore 'didny need any o' this enterprise crap'.

I issued a punishment exercise and told him to mind his language. Sadly, the rest of the class seemed impressed by his bravado.

Tuesday

Another series of late-night window attacks necessitated a further visitation from Greig's Glaziers this morning. The headmaster has asked for more vigilance from Mr Crichton, the janitor, on his evening patrols.

Meanwhile the entire staff, with the exception of Mr Major, found itself incarcerated for a lengthy session of Planned Activity Time this afternoon. Mr Major, interestingly enough, had announced a dental appointment for 4–15 this afternoon, the first in a series of major root treatments which he has managed to schedule for every subsequent Tuesday afternoon until Christmas, a range of appointments which coincide exactly with the planned dates for future PAT sessions.

He claims the timings to be coincidence, but Mr Pickup reckons him to have 'worked a flanker' in an ingenious attempt to avoid the tedium of what he considers a gross waste of his professional time.

Whatever the truth of the matter, he seemed none the worse for wear during our evening meeting to launch his 'Save Our School' campaign. As the meeting's self-appointed chairman, Mr Major made a stirring speech outlining the educational vandalism likely to be perpetrated should the regional council go ahead with the possible closure of Parkland Community High School. Apart from one awkwardly framed question from the floor – which seemed to suggest that Major's new found enthusiasm for the school was not entirely unconnected with his desire to remain an assistant head – he carried it off very well, and has organised a petition as well as a fund raising committee.

For once, he even seemed to carry the support of most of the staff, with the sole exception of Mr Ferguson, head of modern languages. Understandably, Jack Ferguson is unwilling to launch himself into any such campaign, given the imminent announcement of his early retirement, expected to be made official within the next few days.

Wednesday

More window breakages last night. The police have promised to keep an extra watch on the buildings tonight, and not a moment too soon, in my opinion. It would be difficult to fault the speed with which Greig's Glaziers respond to our daily calls for replacement windows, but their constant hammerings are a tremendous obstacle to the creation of a working atmosphere in class.

It was in an effort to escape such distractions during my free period this afternoon that I chanced to wander into the middle staffroom, only to discover the distraught figure of Jack Ferguson hunched over a crumpled letter, his face a mask of bitter vituperation.

'Bastards . . .' he muttered between clenched teeth.

I stopped in my tracks, and raised a solicitous eyebrow. 'Sorry, Mr Ferguson?'

'Bastards . . .' he repeated, a savage edge to his voice as he handed me the torn remnants of a letter from regional headquarters. Unable to decipher its fragmented contents, I made further enquiry of the modern languages principal.

'My retirement, Simpson,' his voice cracked: it's up the bloody chute, isn't it?'

'But how? Why? Surely it was all fixed?'

'Aye,' he lamented. '*Was* fixed. *Was* fixed . . .' His voice tailed off.

'I'm sorry,' I complained. 'I don't understand.'

Obviously still distressed, but calmer now, Ferguson explained:

91

'It's like this, Simpson. We're in for a shortage of teachers in modern languages over the next few years. A couple of months ago, we had too many, and nothing short of bribery and corruption could get you into a half decent job. But now,' – and here his voice perceptibly hardened – 'Now it's all different. And all because those daft buggers at the SED decided to rescue modern languages from the obscurity they deserve and shove them back into the core curriculum instead.'

'But I thought that's what you all wanted?' I queried: 'I thought you all signed a petition to have them *put* in the core curriculum?'

'I did no such thing!' he barked. 'Fifteen hundred other halfwits might have, but not me, sonny, and don't forget it! I wanted out – and *they've* screwed it up for me. God save me from bloody enthusiasts!'

Personally, I think it would be better if Mr Ferguson did retire early. His attitude is the kind that gets teachers a bad name.

Thursday

Good news about the windows: the culprit was caught red-handed last night, and is currently helping police with their enquiries. I didn't have time to enquire about his identity because of my chess club commitment, which continues to be a source of some concern. Membership of the club stands at seventy-eight, with five others suspended last week for fighting during a heated discussion about a queen pawn sacrifice. The lack of funds for any chess sets is proving an insurmountable obstacle to the efficient running of the club, and I was seriously thinking of closing it down until Mr Pickup – not for the first time – became a valuable source of innovative financial advice at afternoon break.

'Here you are, Simpson,' he waved a sheet of paper at me. 'This should solve your chess club problems.'

'What is it?' I questioned.

'A *TALP* funding application form.'

'What's *TALP*?'

'Transition into Adult Life Project – another source of endless ready cash, if my sources are to be believed. Bung down a grant application for your chess sets and see what happens.'

'But I'd hardly qualify for that, would I? I mean, the chess club's not exactly part of an adult life project, is it?'

'Nonsense,' smiled Pickup. 'Highly relevant I'd say. What are most of them going to do once they reach adulthood?'

'Well,' I replied, 'they'll get jobs, I suppose . . .' – Pickup looked scornfully at me – 'or they'll be unemployed . . .'

'Exactly,' finished Pickup. 'And what will they have to fill their days? Endless hours of leisure time. And what better way to spend it,' he concluded triumphantly, 'than in exercising their brains in pursuit of the ultimate opening gambit?'

Doubtful of any successful outcome from such a request to the TALP authorities, I nevertheless accepted the offer of Pickup's ballpoint, and started to fill it in. I await the response with interest.

Friday

An angry confrontation with the headmaster this morning. He summoned me to his study at ten to nine and made the outrageous claim that responsibility for the recent spate of window breakages could be laid at my door.

'Don't be ridiculous, Mr Ross,' I forgot myself. 'How can you possibly –'

'This Enterprise Skills course of yours,' he interrupted. 'Just what does is entail, Simpson?'

'Enterprise Skills? Well: it's . . . um . . . enterprise, sir.'

'Yes, but what do you *do* in the class?' he enquired.

Suspicious that his motives were not entirely based on educational enquiry, I made a guarded response about role-plays and the encouragement of personal initiative.

'Ah, yes,' he confirmed. 'Personal initiative. That's what I wanted to ask you about in more detail. It was, apparently, your little talk on personal initiative which led young Andrew Greig into the paths of unrighteousness . . .'

'Andrew Greig? He's in my class, headmaster.'

'I know he's in your class, cloth-head!' bellowed Ross. 'It's where he got the idea to increase his father's window business by 400 per cent in a single week!'

'Increase his –'

'Don't interrupt, Simpson. Your little exhortation to the class that they . . . um..' – he consulted a police statement held in his right hand –' . . . yes: that they 'get out there and make it happen' has apparently been taken very much to heart by young Greig.'

'But I never thought, headmaster, that –'

'No doubt, Simpson, no doubt. But Andrew Greig did. The replacement of forty six windows in four days has done a good deal to improve the turnover of Greig's Glazing this week. Perhaps, in future, you'll be a little more circumspect about the manner in which you . . .'

I lost the rest of his remarks in a haze of bewilderment, as I later explained to Mr Pickup during our Friday afternoon session at The Pig & Whistle. Pickup was little comfort, to be honest: he spent most of the time cracking awful jokes about Andrew Greig seeing a window of opportunity and deciding to jump through it. He seemed in decidedly good humour, which mood I later ascribed to his news that Mr Major is considering defection to the EIS, for which union Pickup is school representative. His decision is based less on grounds of ethical standpoint over the Anglicisation of Scottish education than on the recent call for industrial action next Tuesday.

'Yes,' confirmed Pickup over our third pint of lager. 'Major says that any union which asks for a strike on PAT days has obviously got its head screwed on the right way.'

Sometimes I despair of our profession.

November

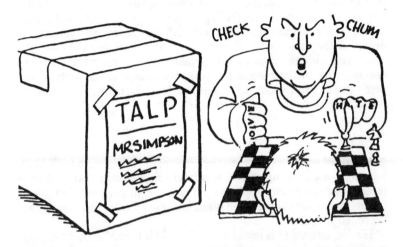

The initiative displayed by Andrew Greig had been a source of much financial consolation to his father. The business provided to glaziers by school vandals is considerable, and any upturn is always welcome. Although not unique to any particular area of Scotland, such wanton destruction is a cause of much financial loss to regional authorities, especially those with schools placed in the larger conurbations.

Meanwhile – and on behalf of all Scottish schools – the EIS continued to complain about an issue which *was* unique to Scotland: the increasing attempts of the government to alter the traditions of their educational system by imposing – at either end of the age spectrum – national testing and city technology colleges, among other things. The Anglicisation campaign gathered momentum, with a series of expensive advertisments in the national press. The 'day of action' at the beginning of November had been a measured success in terms of response, but there were some members of the senior management at Parkland Community High who regarded the issue with a good degree of scorn.

Mr Pickup, however, had been more than satisfied at the response of his members, as his speech – recorded in Morris's next diary entry – will make clear. Morris, for his part, was more excited at the part played by Pickup in securing additional finance for the chess club. After his experiences with Harry McSween and the TVEI money, it had become abundantly clear to Morris that complaints about the lack of money in education, if not entirely false, were not entirely true either. One of the increasing ironies about educational finance in the 1980s became the ease with which money was seemingly provided for 'fancy wee schemes' (as David Pickup called them), compared with the difficulties experienced by principal teachers in ordering the smallest items for everyday class use. Illustrating the point was a parcel which arrived at Parkland during the last week of November.

Monday

A delightful surprise package – the result of my application for TALP funding – awaited my arrival at school this morning. Mr Pickup's recent suggestion that I apply to the Transition into Adult Life Project for augmentation of chess club funds has proved more successful than I'd dared imagine.

Having followed his initial advice to 'go for broke' in outlining my requirements, I was nevertheless astounded to discover that every application for assistance had been met in full. Thus it is that the club now finds itself the proud owner of 40 gleaming chess sets and electronic clocks, a large scale demonstration board and, unbelievably, two top-of-the-range chess computers. The apparent ease with which money is available for such extraordinary funding requests is an obvious source of immediate pleasure, though the irony of apparent shortages in the more mundane areas of curricular requirements will not be lost on Miss Bowman, currently awaiting delivery of her August textbook and stationery requisition.

Fortunately, she was not present to witness the unveiling of such educational munificence, as her in-service course on infusion grammar starts today. We shall be without her services until Friday.

At least the arrival of the chess sets means we shall be able to fulfil our first schools league fixture of the session, a home match on Thursday against St Patrick's Academy, which has a very young but tremendously experienced team. I doubt if we have much chance, but at least it should provide some match experience.

Tuesday

Another dose of Planned Activity Time after school this afternoon. Mr Major – our assistant head – missed the proceedings once again due to his irresponsible arrangement of a regular Tuesday dental appointment, allegedly for root treatment. Nevertheless, prior to his 4 pm departure, he made arrangements for the distribution among staff of his infamous petition to 'Save Our School'. Eager to preclude any untoward recommendations of closure from the forthcoming area review groups, Major has to date collected fifteen hundred signatures, but is anxious to ensure that the full support of staff is enlisted as well.

'They can pass it round during PAT Time this afternoon,' he explained to Mr Pickup at lunch-time. I refrained from pointing out his tautologous addition of the word 'time' to the PAT acronym – hardly a recommendation for his capacities in the English classroom – but was unable to restrain myself when he suggested that the signing of such a petition was 'likely to be the only item of any conceivable interest in the entire bloody afternoon.'

'Really, Mr Major,' I chided him. 'I don't know how you expect much parental sympathy for this campaign if you insist on such a demeaning attitude towards our professional development. It seems to me –'

Unwilling to hear me out, the man had the effrontery to turn and leave the staffroom. Such rudeness ill befits a man in his position.

In point of fact, he was entirely wrong in his forecast of the afternoon's activities, for their interest was considerably heightened by an angry confrontation between Mr Pickup and our depute headmaster towards the end of our staff meeting.

Pickup, having begged Mr Tod's indulgence to make a brief address to those members of his union who were present, seemed to allow his enthusiasm to exceed his discretion: what commenced as a statistical breakdown concerning the success of his euphemistically titled 'day of action' at the beginning of the month became, in effect, a stirring oration regarding the necessity to defend our treasured educational heritage against the sledgehammer mentality of the government. He was just approaching the climax of an unforgettable tirade when Mr Tod broke in:

'Right, Pickup, that's enough. This is a staff meeting, not a TUC conference, y'know.'

'But Mr Tod!' shouted Pickup. 'Don't you *care* about the Anglicisation of our education system?'

'Oh, for God's sake,' snapped Tod. 'Don't give me that again, Pickup. Anglicisation? I very much doubt if you can spell it, let alone understand it!' Pickup looked set to kill, but Tod continued: 'I simply don't understand you lot. If the English were getting all these technology colleges and we weren't, you'd be the first to be up in arms about anti-Scots discrimination. And if the English were getting national tests and we weren't, you'd be hot-foot to Downing Street, asking why *our* children aren't good enough to be tested. And anyway,' he concluded, 'I don't remenber all this fuss when they started comprehensive education down south and sent it up the tracks. I don't recall you moaning about Anglicisation then, do I?' Resting his case, Tod sat back and folded his arms.

I have never seen Pickup so angry. Making an admirable effort to control himself, he nevertheless announced an immediate intention to stage a series of 'wildcat' strikes at Parkland High with effect from the first week in December. A straw-poll among his members indicated divided loyalties over this possibility, though a surprising degree of support was forthcoming from his lady members, not usually noted for their militant stance.

'PAH!' bellowed Tod as he surveyed the serried ranks. 'Bloody Christmas shoppers!' Angrily, he strode from the room.

We spent the rest of the afternoon signing Major's petition.

Wednesday

My third 'please-take' of the week for Miss Bowman. I explained the increasing departmental frustration over her frequent absences to Mr Pickup at morning break, and he was hugely entertained to discover the nature of her in-service course this week.

'God almighty,' he exclaimed: 'Infusion Grammar? What the hell's that when it's at home?'

Reckoning that the intricacies of our latest modular approach to structured language teaching might well be beyond Pickup's grasp of educational theory, I instead outlined the profusion of such courses which my head of department was finding it increasingly essential to attend.

'Mmm,' he mused by way of reply. 'So she never seems to be doing any teaching these days?'

'Not really,' I confirmed.

'Getting further and further away from the classroom, you'd say?'

I nodded gloomy assent as Pickup continued:

'Never sees a kid for days on end, never sets an exercise, never marks a jotter and never raises a stick of chalk to a blackboard?'

'That's the way it seems,' I agreed.

'That settles it!' he declared triumphantly: 'Angie Bowman's in the running for Adviser!'

Thursday

Although initially sceptical of Pickup's allegations regarding Miss Bowman, I find myself increasingly hopeful that he's proved correct. I suspect that she's always had a quiet admiration for my teaching talents, and a close relationship with a future Adviser might do my own career prospects no end of good. Aside from that, there would be an immediate reshuffling within the English department, and I could well stand a chance of a temporary APT post if I play my cards right.

Such thoughts, I confess, were very much on my mind during the chess match this afternoon. Consequently, I found it difficult to remain alert to the various aspects of gamesmanship being employed by the pupils under my charge. Suffice to say that our five-nothing victory over last year's Scottish champions came as something of a surprise, though I would have gladly foregone our two league points after discovering the game-plan of Tony Hammond, our burly captain for the day.

'Congratulations, Tony,' I looked up at him after our vistors had departed in disconsolate fashion. 'How did you manage it? Most of you have only been playing for a few weeks, haven't you?'

'Nae bother,surr,' he growled. 'We claimed them a' fur a sqwerr-go after the gem if any wan o' thim derred tae win. An' they a' crapped it stupit.'

My heart sank.I hope the league secretary never gets to hear of it.

Friday

The return of Miss Bowman at least afforded me a free period for the first time this week. She seems increasingly smug about something:

perhaps Pickup is right about her future intentions, in which case I'd better start preparing a letter of application for my promotion, however temporary.

My position is compromised, however, by the interest I've already expressed in a temporary guidance post which is about to come up. Miss Honeypot of PE (she prefers the appellation 'Ms' but I refuse to bastardise the English language) is about to depart on another bout of maternity leave – a fine, unmarried, example of an APT guidance teacher if you ask me, but that's not the point. I reckon I could fill her shoes more than adequately, and wonder which job I'd stand a better chance of getting.

I discussed the matter with Pickup during our four o'clock pint, and he advised me to apply for both.

Turning the conversation round to Mr Major's campaign to save the school, I was able to impart the distressing news to Pickup that the petition had been sent to – and returned from – the regional education offices.

'Apparently some fool's messed the whole thing up,' I told him, and went on to explain that the authorities had thanked the school for its submission, but had found itself unable to take seriously any such document which purported to bear the signatures of – among others – the Secretary of State for Scotland and his foundling Education Minister. The authenticity of the document had been further compromised, I understand, by the fervent desire to save Parkland Community High which had been expressed by several fictitious characters – amongst whom were numbered Donald Duck and each of his three nephews.

Pickup looked a bit sheepish, and the mysterious authorship of such post-pubescent humour became suddenly apparent.

'But why, Mr Pickup?' I queried him. 'Why on earth did you do that? Don't you *want* to save the school?'

He muttered a dark reply, and suggested I ask no further questions.

Sometimes I wonder what's going on.

December

To Morris, it hardly seemed that a year had passed since the embarrassing débacle of Rose McShane and the Christmas nativity play. So much had happened since then, and he found himself wondering just where the time had gone.

Similarly puzzled at the speed with which events seemed to be overtaking them were several of Morris's colleagues, most notably those in the social studies departments. Having been asked to prepare themselves for the full implementation of Standard grade courses over the subsequent two years, and having been assured that all of the necessary teaching and assessment materials would be provided from central sources, it was with a sense of frustration and increasing concern that they realised just how little help *was* being made available. Parkland planned to implement S grade geography by the coming August – yet here they were in December, and no-one seemed to know anything about it.

Although no longer solely employed as a teacher of geography, it would eventually fall to Andrew Pickup to articulate the anger of his departmental colleagues on the day that the adviser chanced into town. It was to be an unseasonable outburst, so close to Christmas.

Morris, for his part, remained confused over Pickup's unfathomable behaviour regarding Parkland High's potential closure. For one who had so recently advised him to prepare for a hard battle in defence of the place, Pickup seemed to have experienced a somewhat capricious change of heart.

Perhaps, Morris admitted to himself, it was no real business of his. Far better, he thought, to remain aloof from any possible controversy. As the closing weeks of the Christmas term approached, he thought hopefully of his two chances for temporary promotion, and decided that – this Christmas – he would keep a decidedly low profile.

Monday

Our final session of Planned Activity Time has been moved to accommodate the Christmas parties planned for the next three evenings, as well as various rehearsals for Friday's carol service in the local church.

Today's session was given over to Standard grade development work, so we split into departmental divisions. A deplorable example was set by my own department, who seemed to think that the afternoon's proceedings were better devoted to the consummation of seven boxes of mince pies and two bottles of sherry than to a serious consideration of the practicalities surrounding oral assessment.

Such goings-on, however, were as nothing compared to the controversy generated by Mr Pickup during the geography department's session with the social subjects adviser, as I later discovered during a tea-time libation at The Pig and Whistle.

'Fairly embarrassing,' admitted George Crumley, head of geography and Pickup's part-boss: 'I'd asked Pickup to forego his religious education responsibilities for the afternoon so that he could give us the benefit of his accumulated wisdom on S grade geography. I'd gone to all the bother of trundling in Sandy Kingston for an information session on current developments, and this bugger –' he pointed over the bar at Pickup – 'can think of nothing better to do than subject the poor old waster to a torrent of personal abuse which –'

'*I'll* tell the story, George,' interrupted Pickup, and he proceeded to regale us with Mr Kingston's remarks about the current state of readiness for S grade in social subjects.

'Not content,' grimaced Pickup, '– not content with telling us that he didn't have a great deal of new information to give us, and not content with telling us he didn't actually *have* any of the worksheets he'd promised us, nor even the long awaited details of practical assessments he'd promised us, he then had the sheer bloody effrontery to announce that he was here to find out what *we* could contribute to Standard grade, and that he 'wasn't really here to *answer* questions – he was here to *ask* them'. I blew up, I can tell you.'

'Yes,' confirmed George Crumley somewhat drily. 'Asked him what he was getting paid for if it wasn't to answer questions. Told him we could all ask questions ourselves, thank you very much. Told him it was a national disgrace that we still didn't have the faintest idea about what any of us were supposed to be doing. And, finally, told him that he reckoned a three year old child could carry out his advisorate responsibilities very nicely indeed if all they involved was trotting round every department in the region to tell them he didn't have any new information and then insulting their intelligence by asking bloody stupid questions!'

Pickup smiled in proud recollection of his tirade, but Mr Major emerged from behind a pint of heavy and a cloud of pipe-smoke.

'It's all very well, Pickup, but this will all go back to the regional offices, y'know. It's not going to look too good for Parkland High when the closures debate gets properly started. Is it?'

'Perhaps not,' Pickup raised an eyebrow. 'But maybe that's no bad thing either.'

What on earth does he mean?

Tuesday

A concerned enquiry from myself has at last divined the reasons for Mr Pickup's recent animosity towards the school. His frequent attempts to sabotage Mr Major's 'Save Our School' campaign have apparently been caused by his very likely transfer to Rockston Academy, our principal rival in the closure debate, as he revealed to me at morning break.

'Bloody marvellous,' he swore at me. 'They tell me in October that I'm first in line for a principal RE teacher at Rockston – my first chance of promotion in twenty four years – and then they tell me they might be closing the school by the time I get there.

'God almighty! As soon as I start to climb the greasy pole, they start chopping the ruddy thing down!'

My subsequent attempts to persuade him of the economic waste involved in keeping too many schools open for too few pupils was met with enthusiastic and vociferous agreement – as long as it wasn't *his* school they closed down. Sadly, this is the kind of selfish argument which is likely to cause tremendous problems for the region.

At least it explains Pickup's strange behaviour of recent months.

Wednesday

More news on the promotion front, this time with distinct possibilities of advancement for yours truly.

Miss Bowman – in accordance with Pickup's prediction last month – has been made English Adviser, and her consequent departure means that a temporary assistant principal's post becomes available when Simon Young steps into her shoes. My dichotomy over the two APT posts on offer therefore remains, but I have decided to take Pickup's advice and apply for both the English and the guidance positions.

More mince pies and sherry after school to celebrate Miss Bowman's promotion. I tried to remain abstemious, mindful of my pastoral role at the senior dance tonight – the depute head has asked me to do the toilet patrol.

Thursday

Very bad headache. My good intentions regarding last night's celebratory sherry were unfortunately dashed by Mr Major's enthusiasm to 'send Angie Bowman off with a bang'. His subsequent production of a bottle of single malt whisky from beneath his sports jacket was the prelude to an evening better forgotten, but an evening which Pickup seemed especially keen to recall during afternoon break.

'Yes, Simpson,' he declared. 'I think we can safely say that you've brought a new dimension to the term "pupil-teacher relationship".' He paused, ever so slightly. 'Especially after your last waltz with Sandra Lovett.'

'How d'you mean?'

'Oh, come on, Morris,' he laughed. 'Four dances on the trot with the same fifth-year girl, and a slurred offer to see her safely home? Hardly very professional now, was it?'

Alarmed that I could recall very little of last night's proceedings, I was disturbed to learn that I had further blotted my copybook in the depute's eyes by extending my toilet responsibilities beyond their original remit:

'Yes,' Pickup informed me. 'I think Mr Tod's original intention was that you should patrol the boys' toilets only, and leave the girls' ones to the ladies of the staff. Your intrusion of their privacy on the pretext of a vodka raid caused, I understand, a fair degree of personal alarm to several of the senior pupils.'

Embarrassed beyond belief, I dismissed his allegations of impropriety over the toilets and Sandra Lovett, asked him to change the subject, and suggested that – instead of muck-raking – he cast an eye over my completed application form for the APT guidance post.

He glanced through the personal details fairly briefly before turning to what he described as the 'boast sheet'. Having scanned my relatively modest account he suggested that I had little chance of a job unless I could 'tart it up a bit'.

'In what way, Mr Pickup?'

'Look, Simpson, I haven't got time just now. When do these applications need to be in?'

'Oh, not until after Christmas,' I informed him. 'They leave the posts vacant for as long as possible to save some cash, apparently.'

'Right. I'll take this home with me over the hols and bring it back next month – with a boast sheet so good that you'll hardly recognise yourself!'

I accepted the offer and tried to concentrate on recalling my alleged indiscretions of last night. I can't even remember what Sandra Lovett looks like . . .

Friday

The Christmas service. Unfortunately, my eager anticipation of such a joyous and friendly conclusion to the term was sorely disappointed, due in no small part to the appalling behaviour of my second year registration class.

Several of the boys seemed determined to make a fool of the minister, and took great delight in forcing loud and uproarious laughter from their lips whenever he made the slightest attempt to be humorous. I could sense Mr Tod's eyes boring into me as I tried to quell their exuberance along the pew.

Worse still, several of them had obviously been exercising whatever literary bents they possess, for halfway through the first carol it became apparent that an entirely new set of words had been written to accompany *Once in Royal David's City*, words which seemed entirely inappropriate for the occasion. I wasn't too sure how many of the congregation could hear them, but I certainly could and, peering along the row, was horrified to witness Robert Gibson distributing yet further copies of his alternative carol sheet.

Unable to intercept them before the next musical interlude, I was dismayed to hear a growing number of boys close at hand, singing a disgusting version of one of my favourite carols: not content with the usual schoolboy humour about shepherds washing their socks by night, young Gibson's version went on to cast doubts upon the veracity of the Christmas story. In particular, it went on to elaborate an indecent theme which seemed to suggest that the conception of the Virgin Mary was anything but immaculate.

I lunged along the row to confiscate their appalling pornography at once, taking little heed of any who got in my way. Although it caused no small stir, I think I managed to put a stop to their antics effectively enough.

Sadly, Mr Tod didn't agree. He accosted me after the service and told me he'd never seen such an undignified display during divine worship.

'And God knows what the councillors will think, Simpson. The headmaster had five of them lined up at the back to witness the wonderful moral education being bestowed by Parkland High, only to see one of his staff launch a bloody rugby scrum, slap in the middle of the central aisle.'

'I'm sorry, Mr Tod, but –'

'Oh shut up, Simpson,' he quelled me. 'Rumour has it you're in for a guidance post. Is that true?'

'Well, yes, actually, it –'

'Guidance post? Hah!' he barked. 'I wouldn't put you in charge of a flock of sheep, let alone ninety-five first-year pupils!'

Embarrassed at such a display in front of several parents, I coolly offered my best wishes for the festive season and left him alone.

For some reason, Sandra Lovett was standing close at hand. She quietly dropped into step beside me and offered to 'walk me home'. She seems a very pleasant girl, and I was about to accept her solicitous offer when I caught sight of Mr Tod bearing down upon me with suspicious eye and meaningful strides.

I made an excuse about having to decorate the tree and jumped on the nearest bus instead. Another dismal Christmas.

January

The Christmas holidays provided another chance for ponderous reflection by our hero. Inwardly fuming at Mr Tod's scathing denunciation of his promotional chances, Morris nevertheless resolved to ignore the man's snide outbursts in future and devote all his attention to gaining that first important step on the ladder of educational hierarchy.

Foolishly, he also chose to dismiss from his mind the matter of Sandra Lovett: unaware of the romantic effect which his seasonal goodwill had generated with the girl, he assumed her kindly offer to accompany him home on the last day of term had been merely an indication of the girl's friendly personality. If anything more was involved, as Pickup had so crassly suggested, then it would simply be a passing adolescent phase, a temporary crush. This was was to prove a serious misjudgement.

As the new year dawned, however, a report in the local newspaper concerning potential school closures came to Morris's attention. On the first day of the new term, it drove all other thoughts from his mind, and gave cause for tentative hope. Until he met Mr Major.

Monday

The school closure saga continues. I was delighted to read the local newspaper's weekend report that Parkland High has been redeemed from any threat whatsoever, but apparently the matter is not so clear cut as I'd imagined.

'Wonderful news,' I exclaimed to our assistant head Mr Major at morning break: '– about the school being saved.'

'Eh? What's that, Simpson?' he queried.

'The school closures. We're not for the chop after all.'

'Oh?' He raised an eyebrow. 'And who says so?'

'Councillor Malcolm,' I explained, and handed a copy of last Friday's *Parkland Gazette* across the coffee table. It was obviously new to Major, for he spent some minutes perusing the article, shook his head several times, and then broke into a large guffaw of derision.

'Hah! That's torn it!' he barked.

'Something I've missed, Mr Major?'

'School saved, Simpson? I should cocoa! Look at this final paragraph. It says "Councillor Malcolm has given the *Parkland Gazette* his fullest assurance that, whatever else happens, Parkland Community High School will *not* be closed as a result of the review group's recommendations".'

'Exactly,' I chimed in. 'That's clear enough, isn't it?'

'It certainly is,' confirmed Major. 'And gives us a life expectancy of about nine months at the most.'

'But surely the councillor said –'

'What the councillor said,' interrupted Major, 'and what actually happens, are likely to be two entirely different matters. A statement like this –' he held the crumpled newspaper aloft '– will be like a red rag to a bull as far as that review group's concerned. And Councillor Malcolm's never been our greatest friend either – especially after that little fracas you caused at the parish church last month.'

I winced in painful recollection of my attempts to resolve a major disciplinary matter in front of assorted local luminaries at the Christmas service, as Major continued:

'No. It's my guess he's got the closure debate all sewn up but wants to make a show of having tried to save us. But make no mistake: after a proclamation as strong as this one –' again he held the paper aloft '– they're obviously out to get us.'

I told Major he was becoming paranoid about the whole affair and returned to Hut A57 to mark some jotters. Sandra Lovett, an attractive girl from the fifth-year, was lounging around my classroom door for the umpteenth time this month, a fact which Mr Pickup attributes to the excessive attention he claims I paid the girl during last month's Christmas dance. I have tried to dissuade her from such persistent intrusion of my non-contact time, but she always claims academic reason.

This morning it was for some help with her paragraphing. I eventually acquiesced, but she seemed most distracted during the entire lesson. I wonder if Pickup's correct?

Tuesday

Janitorial discontent on the horizon. Mr Crichton, the school care-taker, has grown weary of his daily Augean requirement to clean up the school playground after every interval and lunchtime. The appalling disregard of modern youth for their own surroundings has taken its toll upon our long-serving janitor, who regularly collects a veritable mountain of crisp papers, chocolate wrappings and soft drink cans discarded so thoughtlessly by the vast majority of the school population.

Accordingly, he has informed the headmaster that he will no longer clean it up, as he considers such demeaning labour to be outwith the terms of his contractual employment.

'Or, as he so quaintly put it,' Mr Ross told us this afternoon, 'he's 'no' paid tae clean up a' the manky garbage o' the day'. Accordingly,' Mr Ross continued, 'he told me to "stuff it"!'

'Well, maybe he has a point, headmaster,' I ventured.

A ferocious glower illuminated the ambiguity of my remarks, so I hastily explained myself: 'Not about telling you to stuff it, of course . . .'

'No, Mr Simpson?'

'No, no: perish the thought – but the school does get into a disgraceful mess sometimes. Perhaps we should have some kind of drive against litter, and then –'

'If you'd shut up for one minute, Mr Simpson, that's what I'm about to announce.'

And so it was. Fifteen minutes later, every member of staff had been issued with a detailed battle-plan for the school's anti-litter campaign. All guidance staff are to be heavily involved (my ears pricked up, mindful of my imminent job application), and each and every pupil is to be forcefully reminded of the need to use litter bins.

It was Simon Young, my acting principal teacher, who artlessly broke into the headmaster's final tirade by quietly pointing out that the school playground doesn't *have* any litter bins, and it was little use berating the children for not using something which we didn't provide.

'Eh?' gasped Mr Ross. 'No litter bins in the playground? Is that true, Major?'

'My God,' whispered Mr Pickup, sitting next to me. 'Talk about a finger on the pulse . . .'

A whispered exchange of information ensued, the upshot of which was Mr Ross's announcement that the Parkland Anti-Litter Campaign would be postponed until next month, once a full complement of litter bins has been installed.

Wednesday

More trouble with Sandra Lovett. The girl turned up at my bus stop this morning and offered to 'get me into school'. I thanked her kindly for the offer but, upon boarding the bus, announced a pile of forgotten jotters, and jumped off before she could follow.

She seemed very distressed, but so was I at being forced to catch a later bus. Mr Tod, the depute head, looks unkindly on poor punctuality among the staff, as he was at pains to remind me when I arrived at ten past nine.

'Can't have this, Mr Simpson,' he chided me. 'Especially if you're still intent upon that ridiculous notion of a promoted post.'

His rude snort of laughter infuriated me, and I lost little time in reminding Pickup of his unfulfilled promise to smarten up my job applications for the school's temporary APT posts in English and guidance. He has promised to bring them in tomorrow.

An afternoon 'phone call from the chess league secretary kept me behind at four o'clock. Unfortunately, he's decided to expel my chess team from the schools league after their unexpected victory over St Patrick's Academy some weeks back. Admittedly, it was a victory which owed more to threats of physical violence than to any talent for logical thinking and quiet contemplation, but I considered his decision harsh, and told him so. We shall have to arrange some friendlies instead.

Luckily, I noticed Sandra Lovett waiting for me by the front door, so I escaped through the school kitchens instead. It's all becoming very awkward.

Thursday

Just in time for tomorrow's closure date, Pickup finally remembered to bring in the application forms he's so kindly scrutinised for me. And he wasn't impressed by what I'd filled in: he described my biographical details as 'competent, but hardly awe-inspiring' and my college record as 'a testament to the tedium of teacher-training'. Most of his scorn, however, was reserved for what he termed my 'boast-sheet' which, he claimed, was the ultimate key to getting an interview.

'What d'you mean?' I queried.

'Well, Simpson, look at this guidance one for a start.' he picked up the offending form. 'You say you run the chess club.'

'What about it? I do run the chess club, don't I?'

'Yes, yes – but that's all you've put about it: 'Run chess club in spare time'. That's not good enough.'

'No?'

'No: what you need is something like – um – 'I take a regular and frequent interest in all aspects of extra-curricular activities. I firmly believe that such activities are vitally important to the rounded development of children's personalities.' And then finish it off with – er – 'In particular, my organisation of a daily chess club has allowed me the invaluable opportunity to gain the confidence of a wide variety of pupils in a non-structured, informal context'. That should do it.'

'I see,' I replied. 'Is there anything else?'

Apparently there was. Pickup went through my application with a fine toothcomb until my seven line self-assessment became a three page additional document to the application. My attendance at two in-service courses during four years of teaching was transformed into a 'dedicated commitment to the value of in-service provision, as illustrated by my attendance at various courses on a wide variety of topics, often related to behavioural problems in junior pupils' (we did a half hour session on that at one of Charlie Reckitt's courses).

Furthermore, Pickup suggested that my ill-fated, never-to-be-repeated (though free) school trip to Austria of some years back should suddenly become a striking illustration of my utter devotion to the 'whole-school ethos which is so essential to any guidance teacher worthy of consideration'.

I expressed doubt that any intelligent interviewer could swallow such tosh, but Pickup told me not to assume too much about the interviewers and to get on with writing what he told me. There's obviously more to this promotion business than meets the eye.

Friday

Late to school again, having slept in after a late-night session to complete my application forms in time. Managed to avoid Mr Tod's encompassing gaze by entering through the kitchens again, and quietly popped both envelopes into the office.

'Internal mail, please, Mrs Thomson – for the regional offices,' I smiled confidentially, a finger raised to my lips. 'And – um – perhaps you'd keep this little matter to yourself?'

'Right, Mr Simpson,' she shouted above the din of the photocopier. Turning to one of her clerical staff, she bellowed: 'Hey, Michelle – that's Mr Simpson's applications. Add them to the heap.'

I was shocked at her lack of discretion, but even more surprised to witness a collection of some forty five envelopes similar to my own in two corner piles, a number which seemed to represent virtually every unpromoted member of the staff.

I hope Pickup's given me good advice: this could all be tougher than I'd imagined – especially if I get one of the jobs!

February

Morris Simpson could perhaps have been criticised for a somewhat naive approach to his application for promotion. There have been many unsuccessful applicants in the teaching world who have felt that an ability to *do* a good job effectively came second, in the eyes of the interview panel, to an ability to *talk* a good job effectively and, especially, to prepare a *curriculum vitae* which paints them in the most attractive light possible. David Pickup was simply trying to get his young colleague to the starting blocks at the same time as the other competitors; the race itself was up to Morris. Unfortunately.

Whilst happy to adhere to Pickup's advice on promotion, Morris still found himself unable to fathom the case of Sandra Lovett. Although willing to concede that Pickup's assessment had been more accurate than he had at first realised, he nevertheless refused to admit that Sandra's affection was anything other than temporary. However, the arrival of an extremely large Valentine card on February 14th gave Morris further cause to ponder, and he soon began to realise that something would have to be done.

Meanwhile, Parkland High School was dealing with some of the larger educational concerns which it would have to face in coming years. With the government's determination to introduce a form of local financial management into schools, Mr Ross was keen to prepare for the day when fund-raising and community involvement would mean more than an annual fête to augment mini-bus funds. Soon, he realised, such community liaison could mean the difference between life and death for the school. His litter campaign was only one stage in the process of saving Parkland High. There would be others.

Monday

The headmaster's anti-litter campaign swung into action this morning with the delivery of 45 gleaming yellow litter bins. Having tried to launch his purge on litter last month, and having been subsequently embarrassed to discover the lack of suitable receptacles in the playgound, Mr Ross really seems to have gone to town in an effort to alleviate the problem.

Obviously keen to raise the profile of our establishment – with the councillors as well as the surrounding residents – he has ensured that every bin is proudly engraved with the legend 'Parkland Community High School – Serving the People of Parkland'. Also, mindful of the impending financial revolution in schools management, he has endeavoured to secure local sponsorship for each bin. Although supportive of his laudable initiative, I can't help pondering the ethics of the issue.

While happy to witness an advertisement from the local optician which adorned one of the canisters, I was saddened to realise that Parkland High had accepted paid publicity from the local grocer and off-licence proprietor: it seems especially ironic when one recalls that Mr Ramani is currently under police investigation for supplying large quantities of alcohol to some second year boys before last year's Christmas dances.

My afternoon reverie on the matter, as I supervised a team of litter monitors, was disturbed by the wretched Sandra Lovett. She approached me in the playground with an offer of dubious merit:

'Afternoon, sir,' she smiled sweetly. 'Looking for something to pick up?'

I gazed fiercely at the girl, who has obviously developed an unhealthy affection based on her misunderstanding of my intentions at the fifth-year dance. She dogs my every footstep, and I have had to develop a frosty exterior in an attempt to ward off her unwelcome attentions.

'No thank-you, Sandra,' I replied curtly. 'I'm really extremely busy just now.'

Her bottom lip began to tremble but I turned aside and headed, as swiftly as possible, for the sanctuary of the staffroom.

Tuesday

The beginning of our prelim exams was marked by today's mock examination for English O grade. Simon Young, our temporary principal teacher, has asked me to mark the reading section of the paper, and I found myself burdened with 124 essays to mark after the collection of this morning's papers.

Eager to make a good impression – and mindful of my application for Simon's temporary replacement as APT – I knuckled down to the task over my lunchtime cheese sandwiches. Unfortunately, I failed to make much progress: Sandra Lovett presented herself at the staffroom door for some 'extra hints' before her Higher grade prelim tomorrow. Having disposed of her as quickly as possible, I was further infuriated by a request from Michelle Grant of the fourth year, who came knocking at the door just after 1 pm.

'Surr,' she chewed an odour of spearmint gum in my direction. 'Huv ye goat wurr marks yet? How did ah dae?'

'What?' I drew back a few paces. 'What marks?'

'Wurr exam marks, surr. Mistur Young says yur daein' the markin', surr.'

'Good God, girl – don't be ridiculous,' I explained. 'You've only just finished the first part, and I've only just got the papers. Now leave me in peace, or it'll be even longer before you get them back.'

'Wull we get them tumorrow then, surr?' she tried again. 'Wull we?'

I shut the door on her querulous tones, and returned to the task in hand. Sadly, my afternoon marking was severely hampered by the forty minutes I spent in attempting to mark an essay on a non-existent poem which claimed to be entitled 'Tam O'Shanter In the Snack Bar'. My eventual suspicion that the essay was a 'plant' by one of the exam supervisors was confirmed by a glance at this morning's invigilation list: it was headed, as you might imagine, by my colleague – and erstwhile friend – David Pickup.

116

Wednesday

My attempts to collar Pickup at morning break were curtailed by the headmaster's decision to call a snap staff meeting to announce curricular developments for the school.

'As of next month,' he informed the assembled company, 'Parkland Community High will be welcoming adult students into its classrooms for the first time. We've had several enquiries already,' he explained, 'and each of you will shortly be receiving a list of potential entrants to your classes, with full details of the timetabling implications.'

Mr Ross spoke at some length, but eventually concluded by imploring the staff to support the board of management in this new venture: 'I hardly need to add,' he beseeched us, 'that this move represents the continuation of Parkland High's long cherished tradition of remaining in the forefront of educational trends and curricular reform.'

'Bullshit,' muttered Pickup, sitting beside me and trying to finish his coffee before the end of morning break.

'Pardon?' I queried.

'You heard me,' he whispered. 'The only thing this move represents is the cherished desire of Bob Ross and Simon Major to keep their school open. If they can boost up the roll by getting a few hundred adult bums parked on seats, then the review group's got less chance of closing us down.'

I was angry, not for the first time, at Pickup's cynicism. I informed him that I considered the arrival of adults in the school could only be to everyone's benefit and that – if we *are* to be a community high school – we must be seen to be *serving* that community and its adult members. He countered with the accusation that they'd all had a chance to be at school once, and that they should have 'bloody well appreciated it at the time'.

I got so worked up in the defence of every citizen's right to continuing education that I completely forgot my intention to reprimand Pickup for his childish attempt at humour during invigilation duties yesterday. He really is the limit.

Thursday

I have had to eat my words about adult education classes. Although completely devoted to the principle of ensuring that educational opportunity be opened unto all, I was completely unprepared for the news which broke at our departmental meeting this morning. It concerned the timetable implications, at which Mr Ross had so briefly hinted during yesterday's meeting.

'There you are, Morris,' Simon Young passed me an information sheet. 'That's your new timetable.'

'Sorry?' I asked him. 'How d'you mean?'

'Your new timetable. Starting next month. With the new class arrangements.'

A brief scan of his ill-prepared document led me to the swift conclusion that my current allocation of ten free periods is to be completely halved, and that I am to be responsible for the initiation of an entirely new English course on functional life-skills, aimed at our newest recruits to the classroom.

'But you can't do that,' I complained. 'When will I get my preparation done?'

'Afraid I can, Morris,' he countered. 'With so few pupils in the place, you've done fairly well for free periods up to now. But all I'm doing,' he continued, 'is bringing you in line with the minimum requirement. So you can like it – or lump it.'

Put like that, and mindful of my application for promotion, I really had little choice, so accepted his instructions.

'But you might like this even less,' he continued, quietly passing a list of potential class members across the desk. My eyes skimmed the list fairly quickly, but were drawn up short by the appearance, halfway down, of two adult students whose names had disappeared from my life for ever, and for good. Or so I thought.

'Hang about, Simon,' I smiled across at him. 'Some mistake, surely,' I laughed. 'You've got Rose McShane and Gary Sinnott down here. They left last year – remember?'

'Mmm, I do,' he mused. 'But neither of them could get a job, or even a YTS place. They've decided they want to come back, this time as adult students.'

'But that's impossible!' I croaked. 'We spent most of our time trying to stop them playing truant when they were supposed to be at school, and the rest of it trying to stop their vicious practices while they *were* here. Those two,' I gasped in recollected horror, 'made my life an absolute misery last year. My God, Simon: don't you remember? The fights? The soggy toffee on the classroom wall? The drunken nativity play? They were the living embodiment of original sin!' I declaimed. 'You can't do this to me!'

118

'Morris,' he raised his eyebrows and spoke quietly. 'Don't you *want* to save our school?'

I bowed my head and accepted his decision.

Friday

The only piece of good news to emerge from the week has been this morning's announcement that I'm on the short leet for both of the temporary promoted posts within the school. I imparted the joyous news to Pickup at morning break, but he quelled my exuberance by revealing the composition of the interview panels for both jobs:

'They're both internal posts, so they're both internal interviews,' he explained, before reeling off a litany of names which made my toes curl. Although willing to accept that Simon Young would be on the panel for the English post, and Mr Major for the guidance one, I was horrified to learn that Mr Ross and – especially – Mr Tod, his depute, would be on *both* interview panels. Mr Tod has never liked me.

Unfortunately, my hopes that I might be able to make a better impression on him in the four weeks before the interviews were sorely dashed this afternoon.

To explain, I was just tidying up my desk after the last lesson of the day when I noticed a sealed envelope on my desk, addressed 'To Sir – With Love'. The last pupil having departed, I opened it with some curiosity, only to discover an anonymous poem which purported to express undying affection, not to mention a profound admiration for my physical attributes and mental capacity – in that order, I might add. I was momentarily bewildered about the source of this semi-pornographic epistle, until a demure cough from the doorway drew my attention to the presence of Sandra Lovett within the confines of Hut A57.

'Hello, sir,' she breathed huskily. 'Did you get my letter?'

Deciding that enough was enough, I drew myself up and told the girl a few home truths. I expressed sorrow that she had read so much into our five dances on the trot at the senior Christmas ball, but that she would really have to accept my professional word that I was merely attempting to extend an informal hand of friendship to a pupil under my charge. That was as far as it went, I assured her.

'You're a very pleasant girl, Sandra,' I consoled her, 'but my position precludes any continuation or development of our relationship. I think you'll have to accept that this is just a wee crush you've got, and it'll soon pass –'

Her bottom lip trembled once more, as I concluded with an outright lie:

'And anyway,' I informed her, 'I'm already engaged to a lovely young –'

She screeched in defiance and, to my horror, loosened her tie, undid two buttons on her blouse and thrust her way out of the door., straight into the arms of Mr Tod.

'The filthy beast!' she screamed in my direction, before making a tearful exit for the girls' toilets.

Needless to say, Tod believed her implication and came barging into my room with all the discretion at his command.

'What the hell's going on?' he demanded. 'Touching up the fifth-year, eh, Mr Simpson?'

Speechless with shock, I could only mouth an inarticulate denial before Tod made reference to my forthcoming interview: 'And if I were you, sonny, I'd think up a pretty good excuse before you come along for that guidance post. In fact – if I were you – I don't think I'd bother turning up at all! Let's just hope the girl doesn't press charges.'

That't all I need: an indecent assault charge – and the return of Rose McShane. Roll on the summer holidays!

120

March

It had been a traumatic way to end the week, and the incident with Sandra Lovett made it difficult for Morris to concentrate on his job throughout the next month. Rumours began to circulate, his preparations for interview became increasingly confused, and overshadowing everything was the potential return of Rose McShane to his life.

Parkland High was not, of course, the only school to mount a sustained campaign of adult recruitment. All over Scotland, wherever area review groups were meeting to assess the relative merits of half empty school buildings, headmasters and their deputes had long been drawing up contingency plans. The aim was always the same: to fill empty places and proclaim themselves instrumental in the survival of community values by welcoming adult learners into their ranks. As we already know, such initiatives did not always win the wholeheated support of staff like David Pickup or, in this particular case, Morris Simpson. But then, not every adult class had Rose McShane and Gary Sinnott in its ranks.

In retrospect, it is hardly surprising that Morris Simpson approached the last week of the Easter term – and its accompanying interview – with such conflicting emotions.

Monday

Much apprehension regarding my forthcoming interviews on Thursday, the last day of term. Having been fortunate to appear on the short-leets for assistant principal posts in both guidance and English, I am discovering the drawbacks of such extravagance in promotional applications.

In short, I am becoming extremely confused about which job I would prefer to get: although my initial vocation to teach stemmed from a desire to enthuse young people about the glories of English literature, I have since become increasingly attracted to the pastoral role of the guidance staff, whose commitment to the care and welfare of our young charges is so frequently overlooked by the somewhat blinkered outlook of the secondary specialist.

'Above all,' I explained to Mr Pickup at morning break, 'I don't want them to think I'm just applying for a promoted post willy-nilly. I'd hate them to think I was simply after the extra money.'

'But aren't you?' queried Pickup. 'Isn't that the point?'

I arched a strong frown in his direction and tried, briefly, to explain the wider aspects of a teacher's vocational impulse, but I might as well have saved my breath. A vocational impulse was a concept which seemed completely alien to him.

'Still,' he eventually agreed. 'I can see the point about spreading yourself too thinly. Maybe you should aim to concentrate on one or the other.'

'Oh?'

'Yeh. Make up your mind which one you really fancy and go for it with a vengeance.'

'But that's the trouble: I still don't know which one I'd prefer.'

Pickup's subsequent suggestion that we toss a coin to determine my future career direction seemed to lack appropriate gravity, but I succumbed to his next idea as being the only available option.

'Which interview's first?' he asked.

'The guidance one's in the morning I think, with English in the afternoon. I'm first on each occasion'

'There's your answer, then. Hit them for six with a bowlful of compassion and an in-depth analysis of the horizontal guidance system before they've had time to waken up properly; tell 'em that guidance is *really* your forté, that you only applied for the other job at the suggestion of your extremely supportive departmental colleagues –' at which notion Pickup snorted more rudely than was necessary '– and with any luck they'll believe you.'

I felt somewhat doubtful, but Pickup seemed certain of the approach.

'In for a penny, Morris,' he slapped my back with all the force he could muster. 'Go for it, old son!'

Tuesday

The unseemly row about Sandra Lovett – the fifth year's answer to Lolita – continues to cause me intense embarrassment. Ever since the wretched girl developed an unwholesome attraction towards me after last term's senior dance, I have been engaged in unceasing – and unsuccessful – attempts to ward off her attentions.

Her slanderous accusation of an alleged indecent assault last month remains an extremely irritating source of staffroom tittle-tattle, though I think I've finally managed to convince Mr Tod of my innocence in the affair.

Sadly, there has been no such opportunity to stamp out the vicious *playground* rumours of this distasteful episode, and I discovered my integrity called into serious question by some disgracefully chalked graffiti on my blackboard this morning.

There, in six inch capitals, were the scrawled questionings of prurient adolescence:

'DOES SANDRA LOVETT . . . ?' was the legend which greeted my arrival at registration with 2F. I glared sharply at Gordon Lawson, an unpleasant little boy whose mind resembles nothing so closely as a cess-pit, but he appeared the picture of innocence.

The source of this outrage, however, became abundantly clear once the next class entered. This was my first meeting with the adult life-skills group, initiated by the headmaster in a vain attempt to boost the school role and thereby avoid potential closure. My horror of last month, upon discovering the presence of two former pupils in the group, was as nothing to the dismay experienced when Rose McShane and Gary Sinnot actually walked through the door. It had been true – they *were* coming back!

'Hullawrerr, surr!' bawled Rose, her girth still irredeemably obese, her sideways waddle as distinctive as ever, but her hair now a virulent shade of orange. Sinnot, as morose as before, but dressed anew in complete garb of leather and matching safety-pins, sauntered menacingly to a desk while Rose renewed acquaintance.

'Howzitgaun, surr?' she assaulted my desk. 'Ah heer ye've goat a new burd,' she winked suggestively at the blackboard.

Lurching round to remove the offending words before the rest of the class arrived, I dusted what I now recognised as Rose's copper-plate scrawl from the blackboard.

'Now listen, young lady,' I began. 'If you think I'm going to –'

'Ach, surr,' she chewed across the desk. 'It wiz jist a wee joke. Doan't get yur knickers in a twist . . .'

She lurched towards an empty desk while the rest of the class filtered in. They are an otherwise pleasant little group comprising mainly earnest housewives and old-age pensioners. Sadly, most of them seemed somewhat unnerved by the presence of Rose and Sinnot, who tended to monopolise the lesson. Perhaps they'll come out of their shells tomorrow, when we know each other a little better.

Marked some of their work this afternoon, in fact, and was quite impressed. Thereafter, it was home for some swotting on guidance and, after tea, a trip to the off-licence for a few cans of shandy. Interview preparation can be thirsty work!

Wednesday

A disastrous day. To begin with, I was spotted emerging from the off-licence last night by three of my registration class. What was, in all honesty, a shopping expedition of the utmost innocence has been turned by them into yet another vitriolic rumour concerning my professional integrity.

'Get drunk last night, surr?' queried Gordon Lawson.

'Aye,' chimed in Amanda Scott. 'We saw ye, awright. Five cans o' speshul brew, eh?'

'*And* a wee touch o' the Eldorado?' questioned Sammy Brown.

I spluttered an immediate denial and issued three punishment exercises at once, but by lunchtime a chorus of malicious school-boy gossip had transformed my brief trip to the off-licence into a bacchanalian orgy of awesome proportions. Even my adult class looked mightily suspicious as they came in for the last period this afternoon.

Their apparent uncertainty over my suitability for the profession was sadly heightened by the behaviour of the class's two youngest recruits, Sinnot and Ms McShane. Unimpressed by the modular approach to form-filling, a lesson plan which I had carefully prepared for our second meeting, it took Rose all of twelve minutes to declare herself 'bored oot ma skull', and a further three before she demanded that I show the class 'a vidjo oan the telly'.

Upon learning that the adult life-skills class incorporated no such technological relaxation, she duly proposed the motion – seconded by Sinnot – that the class was therefore 'a loadashite and no' wurrth a tuppny tanner . . .'

I could sense matters getting out of control when Mr Johnstone, a delicately spoken pensioner, demanded that Rose apologise for such bad language and disrespect to her tutor, before asking me whether I was prepared to put up with it. Rose, of course, was incredulous at his request and claimed such freedom of expression as her inalienable right.

It has been a long time since Mr Johnstone was at school, and he has obviously still to come to terms with our less formal approach to education; sadly, however, the upshot was his eventual departure from the classroom followed by four of his elderly contemporaries. They have demanded the return of their registration fees.

I suspect the news is unlikely to please Mr Ross, whose hopes for adult education in the school have been so high. I hope it doesn't affect my interview chances.

Thursday

Interview day. An unmitigated disaster.

Taking Pickup's advice to heart, I set out to make the most of the guidance interview this morning. The opening question (from Mr Tod) made the hardly penetrating enquiry about why I wanted this particular job in the first place, and I launched into the attack.

'Well, I've always felt an affinity for this kind of work,' I tried to convince the blur of panelists across the table. 'It seems to me that guidance is really the most important area of school life, and allows pupils the chance to recognise their teacher as someone who really *cares* for them. The guidance assistant principal can show he knows the kids as people, and –'

'I see,' intervened Mr Ross. 'So you mean he can do this in a way that the subject teacher – or subject APT – is unable to do, Mr Simpson?'

In retrospect, I recollect an edge to his voice when he asked me the question, but at the time I carried on regardless. 'Exactly, sir. As you know,' I continued, 'I've also applied for a post in the English

125

department, but it's probably better that I come clean and admit that the one I'm *really* after is this guidance post. To be honest, I'm not terribly happy about some of the organisation within the English department, and –'

'Mr Simpson,' interrupted the headmaster again. 'This *is* the English interview.'

'Exactly, headmaster, and that's – I beg your pardon?'

'This *is* the English interview,' he repeated quietly, before highlighting the presence on the interview panel of Simon Young, my temporary principal teacher in the department. How on earth could I have missed seing him?

'What? Oh bugger it!' I swore more loudly than intended.

'Yes, well never mind the imprecations,' replied Mr Ross. 'English interviews this morning. Guidance ones this afternoon. Can we take it that you no longer wish to be considered for this one?'

'Yes. I mean, no. I mean . . . well . . . I don't think so. That is – um –' There was a long, pregnant silence: 'Perhaps . . . ?' I beseeched him at last.

'Thank you, Mr Simpson. That will be all,' Mr Ross indicated the door without even bothering to consult his colleagues.

The afternoon was worse. My guidance spiel sounded less impressive the second time around, and Mr Tod chose to bring up the continuing rumours of my illicit liaisons with senior female pupils, and with Sandra Lovett in particular. He also made enquiry of me concerning allegations of outdoor drinking sessions, as related by the parents of some second-year pupils to whom he had just been speaking. Finally, and most unfairly, he questioned whether it was sensible to appoint to any position of responsibility a teacher who seemed to have difficulty in controlling a class of old-age pensioners!

His web of half-truths and deceit shocked me into dumbfounded silence, especially when he asked me to deny the charges.

'Well, Simpson,' he demanded. 'Are they true, or aren't they?'

I gazed sadly across the interviewing table: Mustering as much of my dignity as remained, I posed the eternal question: 'What is truth?' Tod looked pretty vacant and obviously failed to recognise the allusion. Drawing myself up from the chair, I left the room and did not wait for answer.

I don't think I got the job.

Good Friday

First day of the Easter break. Pickup telephoned at 10 am with confirmation that both jobs had gone to other candidates and to offer commiserations.

He suggested we meet for a lunchtime pint and the opportunity to drown my sorrows. I accepted without demur.

April

It would probably be little comfort to Morris, but his appalling interview probably had little effect on his chances of getting either job. In particular, his hopes for a guidance post were severely handicapped by his subject teaching qualification, a point which David Pickup eventually explained to him some weeks later.

For the moment, however, he was disconsolate. He wondered, briefly, about applying for one of the new senior teaching posts which the government had allowed to be created after the 1986 pay settlement, posts which were designed to reward the practising teacher who preferred to stay in the classroom instead of seeking advancement in the promotional jungle. Again, Mr Pickup was to prove the source of sound advice.

Meanwhile, the government was intent upon pushing through a multitudinous array of alternative educational reforms. Michael Forsyth, the minister for education and health, continued to set a frantic pace: in early 1989 he had set in motion the distribution of preliminary information on the composition of school boards; by the end of the year, school boards were to be in place throughout all of Scotland's state schools, if the minister was to have his way. Those more cynical observers reckoned such indecent haste was in no small part due to Forsyth's enthusiasm to have school boards which – by the likely nature of their composition – would encourage 'opting out' of local authority control to be funded instead by central government.

The EIS, for its part, mounted a counter attack of newspaper and television advertisements, public awareness campaigns and sticky-badge distribution. The major thrust of the campaign was its determination to extol the virtues of Scottish education, and its members' enthusiasm for opting *into* the system, rather than out of it.

At Parkland High, the more immediate concern of Mr Major was to ensure the survival of the school, not to mention his continued employment. The beginning of April brought worrying news of closure, though Mr Major, as so often before, eventually reckoned upon a way of turning circumstances to his own advantage.

Mr Pickup, however, considered the decision to have been inevitable from the start . . .

Monday

The school closure row has boiled over once again. Our battle appears to have been lost, despite the valiant efforts of Mr Ross, the headmaster, to attract adult students and achieve community school status. We discovered today that the local review group has judiciously leaked its intentions to close our extremely dilapidated building – and merge us with Rockston High, a slightly *less* dilapidated building some three miles distant.

'But I thought we were going to be saved,' I exclaimed to Mr Pickup this morning. 'After all, the region's just spent thousands of pounds on our new language laboratory, and even more on fitting us out with carpets to replace the old linoleum . . .'

'Mmm,' he mused. 'A bit ominous, wasn't it?'

'Ominous? How d'you mean?'

'The fact they were spending all that cash on us. Usually a prelude to closure, in my experience.'

'Oh, don't be ridiculous, Mr Pickup. A responsible public body's hardly going to waste taxpayer's money by –'

'Hah!' Pickup barked. 'Don't give me that! Responsible public body? The same one that repainted Whitebank Academy after years of neglect – then closed it down twelve months later? The same one that builds acres of flat-roofed buildings and then spends millions of pounds every year welding cartloads of new felt on top of them? The same one that put fitted carpets into every corridor and office of this

129

school last month – and then didn't provide a hoover to clean the ruddy things?'

'Didn't they?'

'Of course they didn't! Tod was fuming last week: his cleaner got fed up with the manky state of the carpet and mopped a soapy bucket of water across it one night. It was still oozing bubbles three days later. He ended up with duck-boards from the door to his desk.' Pickup sniggered. 'Hardly very impressive when you're interviewing prospective parents for next year's intake!'

Momentarily amused at the thought of our irascible depute's discomfort, I was nevertheless amazed at Pickup's disclosures. If what he says is true, who knows *what* the region might do about closing us down?

Tuesday

Our new temporary APT guidance took up his post today. Despite bitter recollections of an interview last month for the selfsame position, I swallowed my pride, bit an anguished lip, and proffered a welcoming hand at morning break.

'Good morning,' I introduced myself. 'My name's Simpson. Morris Simpson.'

'Ah!' he exclaimed with glee. 'So *you're* the one, then?'

'Sorry?' I apologised, uncertain of his drift.

'*Teacher's Pet In School Love Triangle,*' he drew an imaginary headline across the air. 'Sandra Lovett, eh? Bet she does – eh? Pleased to meet you, Morris –' he nudged me suggestively in the ribs '– the Humbert Humbert of Parkland High, or so I'm reliably informed. Frank Parker's the name: pleased to meet you –'

I withdrew my hand immediately. 'Don't believe everything you're told,' I glared icily at him, incredulous that my embarrassing relationship with one of the senior girls is evidently still causing such malicious and ill-founded gossip among the staff.

Slightly distracted, I tried to initiate a conversation on the merits of Parkland's guidance system, but the man seemed completely at sea. Unbelievably, he failed to appreciate the difference between a horizontal guidance system and a vertical one, let alone the fact that we're now moving towards a system of shifting area responsibilities within the guidance framework.

'But didn't you cover any of that on your guidance courses?' I enquired of him.

'Don't know,' he replied. 'Never been on one.'

My jaw dropped as the bell signalled the end of morning interval and Parker walked off to his classroom. How on earth did he get the job, then?

Wednesday

Study leave began for senior pupils today, and Mr Major took time off from masterminding his 'Save Our School' campaign to organise the draw for the annual Scrabble championship. As usual, I am unable to avail myself of the extra free periods afforded to many of my colleagues by the departure of their senior classes: my timetable's preponderance of first and second-year pupils leaves me little time for such lexical enthusiasms.

In fact, the closest I get to a senior group is the loosely termed 'adult life-skills class', a rapidly dwindling group of pensioners and housewives, whose membership continues to be depleted by the appalling behaviour of Rose McShane and Gary Sinnot.

Sadly, I lost another two class members this afternoon. Unbelievably, it had taken Miss Melrose four full weeks to appreciate that she was *not* enrolled in a 'German for Beginners' class, as she had fondly imagined, whilst Mrs Hart took strong exception to the grossly abusive language used by Rose and Sinnot during our improvised job-interview rehearsals.

I confided my fears for the future of the class to Simon Young, my temporary principal teacher, and he wasn't too pleased.

'Listen, Morris,' he outlined firmly. 'The headmaster's got a lot of money riding on this one. You know he sees adult numbers as our only saving grace in the closure battle, and I don't relish telling him you've already decimated the class. Get them something interesting to do: we want to grab them now – and keep them.'

I asked for some practical suggestions, but the most exciting thing he could offer was a visit from one of the poets in the 'Writers in Schools' scheme. I told him it was hardly very relevant to the theme of their course, but he countered with the premise that poetry was relevant to *all* walks of life.

'And at least,' he continued, 'it'll give you a free period or two while the writer does his stuff . . .'

Maybe there's something to Simon's idea after all. I told him I'd investigate the possibilities.

Thursday

A mysterious incident this morning: just after registration I met Mr Major, a bulky parcel under his arm and a guilty frown across his face, emerging from the hut I share with Mr Pickup.

'Morning, Mr Major,' I heralded him. 'How's the campaign?'

'What? Oh – fine, fine,' he muttered, before scurrying away to the main building.

'Not like him,' I remarked to Pickup as I entered our shared store-cupboard. 'He's usually keen to spread the latest closure gossip.'

'Mmm,' Pickup murmured, obviously distracted as well. Further enquiry revealed that he was searching for a bundle of union literature and promotional material. As EIS representative, he had been due to distribute badges and car stickers at morning break, items which would proclaim his union's willingness to remain within the structure of state Scottish education, rather than follow the anglified notions of intrusive government meddlings.

'Damned if I can find them, Morris,' he complained. 'And I'm sure I left them on this shelf last night.'

'You'll need to be a bit more organised,' I chided him, 'if you're still keen to get the principal's RE job at Rockston.'

'Hah!' he barked, and his attention shifted at once from the fruitless search. 'Don't bring that one up! The whole thing's frozen until after the closure débacle's sorted out. Honestly! First they tell me I'm certain to get it, then they pull the carpet out from under by telling me it's all up for grabs until after the merger decisions are taken. I might even have to re-apply for my own job here. Talk about organising a piss-up in a brewery!'

I muttered some consolatory words and outlined my bewilderment at the whole promotion structure, not least my thoughts on the unsuitability of Frank Parker for a guidance post.

'Oh well,' explained Pickup. 'That one was easy enough to see coming. If I'd known there was a physics teacher in for the job, I'd have told you to chuck out your application straight away.'

'Why?' I queried.

'Because he's a physics teacher.'

'I know. But what's that got to do with it?'

Pickup sighed patiently and explained, at some length, that promotion within the pastoral hierarchy usually had more to do with subjects taught than with suitability for the chosen post.

'Look at us,' he said. 'One physics teacher instead of three, and it's been that way since last August. Ross has been screaming for a physics bod from staffing without success and then, lo and behold, one applies for a guidance job. What d'you *think* he's going to do? Give it to an English teacher? You lot are ten a penny, old son.'

'In that case,' I slowly pondered the repercussions of his remarks, 'is there any point in me applying for the senior teacher post that's coming up for here next month?'

Pickup looked scornful. 'Can you teach physics, chemistry, maths or modern languages?'

I shook my head.

'Forget it!' he scoffed.

Friday

Mr Major's campaign to save the school swung into top gear today. He called a lunchtime meeting of all staff, which regrettably attracted only a 40 per cent turnout, most teachers being otherwise engaged at The Pig and Whistle during Friday lunchtimes.

Major retained a childlike enthusiasm, nevertheless, for the next stage of his operation. After forcing us to watch an appallingly produced video outlining the immense benefits already accruing to schools piloting the school board experiment, Major went on to detail his plans for the continued survival of Parkland Community High by initiating a similar board ahead of other schools in the region.

'That way,' he explained, 'we can opt out before they close us down.'

A stunned silence greeted his revelation.

'Opt out?' queried Simon Young. 'Surely we don't need to go that far, Mr Major? Can't we appeal to the government first?'

'No chance,' countered Major. 'We'd need to have 80 per cent of the school's places filled. Unfortunately, we can only muster a 60 per cent roll – and that's counting Simpson's adult class as well as all the dinner ladies. Nope – I'm afraid it's opting out or closure, as far as I can see.'

A heated debate ensued, but the upshot was Mr Major's continued enthusiasm to 'screw those bloody councillors', as he so quaintly put it, by 'getting out and running the whole damned show ourselves.'

I sensed a division among the staff present, but Major plans to have a school board up and running by the end of the session. We shall see, but I don't think he'll have the support of Mr Pickup, for one. The mystery of my colleague's disappearing stickers was solved when Major produced his own campaign materials.

These comprised, in the main, a badge and a car-sticker for each member of staff, items which bore an overwhelming resemblance to those which had gone missing from Pickup's cupboard. There were, however, a couple of fairly dramatic alterations to each sticker and badge: where it *should* have said 'Scottish Education – I'm opting *IN*', each item now bore the legend – carefully Tippexed and rewritten by J.P. Major – 'Parkland Community High – I'm opting *OUT*!'

I'm not sure I approve of Major's methods, but I suppose he has the school's interests at heart. I took a sticker anyway, and promised to put it on my saddlebag.

The fight begins in earnest.

May

Mr Major's proposal to form a school board ahead of the goverment's already hasty timetable owed much to his self-interested enthusiasm, and little to a realistic appraisal of the situation.

Whatever the eventual outcome of school boards, reaction from parents in those early months ranged from apathy to antagonism. Many parents were happy to concede that they would welcome a greater degree of information from schools, and would indeed be happy to share with staff in some of the more everyday matters pertaining to running them. Very few, it seemed, wished to have the wide-ranging powers to oversee the appointments of senior staff and approve expenditure plans, as allowed for in the government's design.

Time would, of course, eventually tell whether the government knew what parents *really* wanted, as opposed to what they *thought* they wanted. For the moment, however, most head teachers had the utmost difficulty in drumming up a quorum to attend initial explanatory meetings about their respective school boards – and they didn't expect it to get better when they got round to electing the real things.

It was probably just as well, however, that at least someone in Parkland High was trying to do something positive about keeping the school open. Mr Ross's alternative scheme – that Parkland Community High become the area's principle adult learning centre – had run into problems all of its own. They would get worse.

Monday

The continuing decline of my adult class gives further cause for concern, and I have agreed to my principal teacher's suggestion of 'importing some outside talent. Simon Young's idea to apply for a visit from one of the 'Writers in Schools' people has been met with a surprisingly swift reply from the Arts Council: their letter to the effect that Adrienne Chambers will come and speak to the group on Friday has caught me with my trousers down, so to speak. Never having heard of the ruddy woman, I had to make a hasty foray to the local library at the weekend, and accordingly spent much of today putting several of her poems on to Banda masters.

My efforts were appreciated by much of the group, though Rose McShane – whose immature disruptions have already decimated class numbers – seemed unable to appreciate the delicate imagery outlined in *Seeking a Framework*, one of Miss Chambers' most hauntingly affectionate works.

'Loada garrbidge!' she pronounced judgement upon a first reading of the work, and further study by the rest of the class was rendered pointless by her continued interruptions to demand a 'coaffy brekk'.

Gently, I tried to suggest that she give Friday's class a miss, but she seems intent upon making her presence felt . . .

Tuesday

Mr Major's plans to save our school from threatened closure and subsequent merger with Rockston High took on tangible form with his announcement of tomorrow evening's meeting to form a pilot school board ahead of the government's timetable. He has already circulated parents and interested parties with nomination forms, and hopes to have a board up and running by the end of term, whereupon he plans a parental ballot to opt out of local authority control.

Sadly, his plans have failed to gain the support of all the staff, who fall into two fairly distinct camps: approximately half of them look forward to the possibility of opting out – and a consequent liberation from the endless plethora of regional documentation which regularly finds its way into their pigeon holes; the other half – mainly younger staff – view with horror their future chances of promotion beyond the confines of Parkland High, and have accordingly given a massive 'thumbs-down' to Major's suggestion.

And then there is Mr Pickup, who falls into a camp of his own – as he explained to me over morning coffee.

'The guy's a sneaky wee bastard,' he swore across the table, obviously still smarting from Major's distribution of suitably amended EIS promotional material last month, material which now proclaimed Parkland's enthusiasm for opting out of authority control instead of his union's enthusiasm for remaining within it. 'He's never given a toss for the school before now – he's only in it to save his own job, y'know.'

I expressed general agreement, but pondered aloud on the possibility that Pickup's own views were not entirely free from self-interest, given the uncertainty of future principal teacher posts in religious education at Parkland and Rockston.

Tellingly, he shifted the conversation at once, and enquired of my own prospects for a senior teacher post.

'I've decided not to apply,' I informed him. 'I don't think I've got the necessary experience behind me yet.'

'Huh!' he shrugged his shoulders. 'I wouldn't let that stop you. It hasn't bothered anyone else.'

'Really?'

'Ach, yes – it's worse than the guidance scramble of the 1970s: every bloody teacher who hasn't managed to rise above the rank of private – in two years or twenty, mind – has sudenly decided that being a senior teacher is what it's all about. Endless proclamations of loyalty to the kids and devotion to classroom teaching – and a pair of greedy little eyes fixed on an extra thousand a year for doing sweet fanny adams – or so they think until they get the prelim timetable to organise!'

'But administration won't be part of their remit, surely? Their posts were created to recognise the contribution made by those who'd decided to remain within the strictures of classroom teaching, and –'

'The FOP, eh?' Pickup interrupted.

'The what?'

'The FOP – Faithful Old Plodder. And that's what I thought when they started it all up; but don't you believe it, Simpson. What they look for in a senior teacher is a DYT, and one who –'

'A DYT?'

'Yep: Dynamic Young Thruster. Someone who's happy to do all the donkey work of arranging photocopying rotas and tuck shop duties – the kind of thing that old Major's supposed to be paid for – and who mistakenly believes it'll lead to higher things in the long run.

'And I suppose you're probably right,' he concluded. 'You're no

137

really a FOP yet, even if they *were* looking for one. And as for being a Dynamic Young Thruster –' he snickered into his coffee cup '– I suppose Sandra Lovett's the only one who can tell us about that.'

I ended the conversation at once, and told Pickup I was getting heartily sick of his sordid and adolescent humour. Fortunately, Sandra leaves school next month, and the rumours surrounding my relationship with her should simmer down after that.

Perhaps I'll go for a senior teacher's post in the next round of applications instead.

Wednesday

Mr Major spent much of the day preparing our assembly hall for tonight's school board meeting. I suspected his decision to lay out seven hundred chairs verged on the optimistic, but kept my own counsel on the matter.

Meanwhile, the headmaster called a brief meeting at afternoon break to warn staff of a politically motivated group of subversives who have been distributing literature at the school gates recently. He has asked us to be on the look-out for any strangers in the vicinity:

'You can't miss them,' he explained succinctly. 'They look as if they've just come out of a doss-house. If you catch them at it, let me know at once and I'll 'phone the police.'

It's distressing to realise how these activists try to twist the minds of our young people. Vigilance is clearly required.

Thursday

Mr Major's inaugural school board meeting appears to have been something of a flop. Only twenty four people turned up last night, nine of whom left upon discovering that the jazz society was being held in an alternative classroom.

Of the fifteen participants left behind, Major found insurmountable difficulties in composing a school board, as Pickup took great delight in telling me at morning break.

'He only got three nominations to begin with, and one of *them* had to be discounted when he discovered who it was.'

'Oh?' I queried.

'Yep. Michael Hunter's dad had put his name forward.'

'And what's wrong with that?'

'The guy's in jail, Simpson, and will be for the next four years.

Bit difficult attending board meetings under the circumstances.'

'I see. And what about the other two?'

'Mrs Batey, an interfering old busybody if ever there was one, and Tom Montgomery, our prospective Conservative councillor in next year's district elections. Still,' he mused aloud, 'if Major gets another half dozen or so before the end of term perhaps we'll have a school board in time for August – by which time they'll probably have closed us down anyway.'

I can't help feeling sorry for Major, who's put such a lot of effort into the campaign. Maybe I should offer to stand as one of the staff members myself . . .

Friday

A day of considerable embarrassment. The omens were inauspicious from the moment that Rose McShane met me after morning break, and announced that she was looking forward to meeting 'that poetry wumman and tellin' hur werr tae get aff'.

I urged restraint and asked her to respect the other members of the class and their desire to meet the poet, if not respecting the fact that Adrienne Chambers was a famous literary figure.

'Faymuss?' squawked Rose. 'Faymuss? Hus she ivver bin oan telly? Hus she. Eh?'

'Not to my knowledge, Rose, but I hardly think –'

'If she's no' bin oan telly, surr, she's no faymuss.' Her judgement complete, Rose marched in the direction of the tuck-shop, announcing her intention to buy some popcorn 'furr the show'.

I shuddered at the prospect, but hurried to the office to welcome our guest.

Unfortunately, the school's front door was blocked by a scruffy looking individual who appeared to have wandered off the street in search of refuge. He looked a most unsavoury figure and was clad in a pair of moth-eaten denims and a collarless shirt which obviously hadn't seen a washing machine for several weeks. Mindful of the heamaster's recent instructions about political activists, I took him gently by the shoulder, turned him in the direction of the front door, and quietly asked that he leave the building before I found it necessary to contact the police.

'Excuse me,' he grimaced in a slow, deliberate, and slightly effeminate voice, 'but I'm waiting for a Mr Simpson of the English department. I'm due at 11 o'clock for a poetry reading.'

I froze in my steps, as he shrugged away: 'And take your hands *off* me,' he lisped. 'I don't know where you've been.'

'Um. Yes. Certainly. Terribly sorry,' I stammered an introduction. 'Actually, I *am* Mr Simpson. Morris Simpson. And you must be – um – *Mister* Chambers? Terribly sorry,' I repeated. 'Um. It's just that I expected . . .'

'Yes?' he glanced sharply at me.

'Um. Never mind. Ah . . . welcome, anyway, to Parkland High. It's my class you've come to see, and, er . . . they're all looking forward to meeting you immensely.'

'Yes, well let's get a move on, shall we? I haven't got all day. Could you sign this, please, to say I've been?' He handed over a regional visitation document: 'Otherwise I don't get paid.'

Thereafter, the day went from bad to worse. It took the class a long time to accept that Adrienne Chambers was a man, and it may take me even longer to live down my mistake, news of which was all round the staff by lunchtime.

The actual poetry reading was a disaster. Apart from the rather unpleasant odour of patchouli oil which seemed to emanate from our literary visitor, there was the matter of his extremely unconventional dress as well as a series of extravagant, outlandish affectations and gestures which he insisted upon using when reading his poems. When she was not munching popcorn, Rose McShane could hardly contain her amusement, and finally broke into a loud guffaw of derision when Chambers produced a collection of slate and brick objects which he quaintly termed 'concrete poetry'.

'Hah!' she declaimed. 'Witta loada bluddy mince! Ye meen tae say yoo get *money* fur doin' crap like that? Ah've seen –'

I broke in to call a halt but, for once, the entire class agreed with Rose. Mr Hayman suggested that the whole affair was a complete waste of everyone's time and put forward the motion that we abandon today's lesson with immediate effect. Support was forthcoming from all of his colleagues, and a mass walk-out ensued, along with seven further resignations from the course as they walked past my desk. The headmaster will be furious.

I began a profuse apology to Mr Chambers, but he appeared totally unconcerned and began to make his way towards the door.

'Happens all the time, darling,' he smiled sweetly, and muttered something about prophets being without honour, before tucking his visitation form into a grubby hip pocket. Suddenly, I realised why he'd been so keen to get it signed before the performance started.

In a final conciliatory gesture, I offered to take him for lunch, though it was with some relief that I greeted his refusal. The bell rang to signal the morning's end and, for the first time in my teaching career, I decided to join the Friday lunchtime exodus to The Pig and Whistle. I needed a drink.

June

David Pickup's cynical attitude towards the creation of senior teacher posts was not unique. It echoed a widely held belief that, with seven thousand appointments to be made by 1992, many authorities were viewing the jobs as another, initial, step on the promotion ladder. It was hard to reconcile their denials with the frequent appointments of relatively inexperienced staff – no matter how go-ahead and dynamic their ideas – to the position of senior teacher, a position which had been meant to reward those who had remained within the strictures of the classroom over a lengthy career.

As usual, however, weightier matters of more local significance concerned the denizens of Parkland High. Mr Tod's revised time-table, which had started in May, was beginning to create problems all of its own. And the annual visits of the new intake, arranged with feeder primaries for the last week of term, were beginning to be more of a burden than had ever been imagined possible.

Most importantly of all, of course, there was still the question mark over Parkland's future: would this be its last session in full existence? The education authorities had still to reach a final decision, and Morris hoped that news of his adult class numbers hadn't reached their ears . . .

Monday

Today saw the official disbandment of my adult life-skills class. Its original intention of boosting the roll in an attempt to ward off our school's closure has been rendered impractical by the fact that all but three of its original members have voted with their feet and abandoned the course. With the school's future still hanging in the balance, Mr Ross has been little impressed by my contribution to the closure battle, and even less so by my attempts to provide community education for all.

Needless to say, one of our three remaining members was Rose McShane, at whose door I lay most of the blame for the course's failure. She seemed nevertheless distressed when I informed her that today would be our final meeting.

'Aww, surr,' she complained. 'That's no ferr. Jist when ah wis startin' tae get the hang o' all this interview crap.'

I shuddered in recollection of her quasi-literate contributions to my carefully devised oral role-play simulations, and quietly wished her well for the future. Privately, I am delighted to realise that the name McShane will never darken my register again.

The removal of her class from my timetable has also allowed me an extra few hours of preparation each week, at least until August when the new first year arrive. Having moved on to our new timetable last week, I am having to keep up to the mark with lesson plans and the like. I'm delighted to report that my principal teacher has entrusted me with the top section for Standard grade English ('Not that we stream them, mind,' he cautioned me when handing out class lists at the relevant departmental meeting), and I am looking forward immensely to the challenge.

Tuesday

Widspread confusion over the new timetable. Mr Tod, having convinced us last year of the benefits to be derived from starting a new timetable in May, has seen fit to alter his original plan with a degree of what he quaintly terms 'fine-tuning'.

Basically, he was unhappy about the plethora of Monday holidays which appear in the course of any one academic year and the consequent loss of teaching time to certain departments. Coincidentally, the maths department – for whom Tod himself occasionally takes a lesson – was one of the worst affected. Accordingly, in an ill-judged attempt to alleviate this loss of teaching time he has instituted a six-day week for next session.

Briefly, this means that the timetable's first week started on a Monday two weeks ago and finished, not on Friday but on the subsequent Monday. Week Two began last Tuesday and finished today, with Week Three due to start tomorrow, Wednesday. It has all been too much for Mr Pickup, whose religious education classes have been thrown into a confusion not entirely of his own making.

'Organised bloody chaos!' he swore across the coffee table this morning. 'There I was with a video, all set up and ready to go for the fourth year. And who walks in but 2P, ready and eager to start their Ayatollah Project! I've just finished telling them we're still in Week Two, not Week Three, and that this is really day six, not day one, when Craig McDonald from 3F arrives. Unfortunately, he's still under the impression that we're in the timetable for *last* session. By the time I get *him* sorted out, and the second-year despatched to home economics, it's too bloody late to start the video with the fourth-year, who've all been off to the gym for a double PE and have had to get changed back into civvies when Bill MacDuff tells 'em they're in the wrong place at the wrong time.

'Honestly,' he continued in bitter recrimination. 'Tod's had some daft notions in his time, but this one takes the biscuit. Not only do the fourth-year miss their video, which has to go back today, but the entire frigging school's thrust into chaos and disorder, and all because that ruddy man couldn't organise a Sunday-School picnic. He really is the absolute limit! If he doesn't waken up his ideas, I'm thinking of going above his head, and if –'

I interrupted, before he became too overwrought.

'Mm,' I agreed non-committally. 'Too bad about the fourth-year. What was the video about, anyway?'

Pickup grimaced fiercely. 'Tolerance,' he spat out, apparently oblivious to the potential irony. I made some broadly sympathetic noises, and went off to teach the third year. Or was it the fourth?

Wednesday

The school has been saved! Our reprieve was announced today, and the headmaster called a special staff meeting at 3 o'clock.

'I've closed the school early,' began Mr Ross, 'to impart news of some magnitude. The education authorities have informed me this afternoon that both Rockston High *and* Parkland High will remain open for the education of this district's children.'

Sporadic outbursts of applause were mingled with occasional oaths of displeasure from some of our less loyal staff, but Mr Ross continued regardless:

'The authority's statement explains – and I quote – 'that the area review group sought the opinions of a supplementary review group. This review of the review group's original recommendations has reassessed the position regarding Parkland and Rockston High Schools and the conclusion has been reached that greater priority should be given to the overall educational provision within the district. Although both schools have an approximate take up rate of only 55 per cent of available places, it is nevertheless recognised that plans for the innovative use of surplus accommodation should be given the chance to come to fruition. In addition, the authority is pledged to accord the best possible teacher/pupil ratio in such an area of multiple deprivation and priority treatment, and the ratios currently enjoyed by both schools would be severely disadvantaged should a merger occur between them.'

'It goes on,' explained the headmaster, 'to claim that the fact that both schools have split sites – originally a reason for suggesting at least one closure – has now come to be recognised as a positive advantage instead, allowing pupils to experience a wide and healthy range of climatic conditions, rather than being cooped up inside a centrally heated building all day.'

He grimaced wryly, as several members of staff proved unable to conceal their scorn, but struggled gamely on:

'And finally,' he concluded with a benevolent smile directed towards Mr Major, co-ordinator of the 'Save Our School' pressure group for Parkland High, 'the authority finds it incumbent to "acknowledge the bitter feeling which potential closure has brought to the fore from parents of children at both schools. It concedes that it is the council's task to serve the people, and if the people have declared that both schools should remain open, then remain open they shall".'

'In other words,' whispered Pickup beside me, 'the councillors have got the shits.'

'Mr Pickup!' I hissed fiercely.

'Can you offer another explanation?' he whispered back. 'Two half-empty schools, both of them falling apart at the seams but still having money pumped in like there was no tomorrow – and both situated in highly marginal council constituencies. Give us a break, Simpson!'

I refused to be drawn into such a pointlessly indelicate argument, and suddenly recalled the obvious reason behind his displeasure.

'I suppose,' I questioned him, 'this means the end of your aspirations for a principal's RE post at the newly merged Rockston?'

'Aah, shut it!' he barked, and left the room right in the middle of Mr Ross's valedictory message of congratulation and exhortations for greater efforts in the continued service, next session, of Parkland Community High School.

How rude can you get?

Thursday

A more positive air of optimism surrounded the school after yesterday's news, and it was good to welcome several further classes from our feeder primaries on this week's primary/secondary integration visits. It's very heartening to see their fresh and eager faces, slightly apprehensive but obviously very excited at the prospect of coming to the 'big school'.

I have been given a first year registration class next session, many of whom I shall meet during tomorrow's visit. I spent some time this afternoon preparing a little speech of welcome to set them at their ease – they'll probably all feel very nervous about it all.

Friday

My expectations of the new first year have been somewhat disappointed. Far from appearing nervous, the great majority of my future registration class would appear to be hardened school-warriors, only too eager to make their own distinctive mark upon Parkland High School.

In particular, fifteen of our young male visitors from Parkland Primary School decided to involve themselves in a yo-yo competition with our current first (or rather, second) year. Unwilling to extend the hand of sporting friendship when they lost, several of them launched a vicious attack upon their elder brethren, using the aforementioned yo-yos as flailing weapons of terror rather than for their original purpose of demonstrating manual dexterity. A pitched battle ensued, which Mr Pickup and I only managed to quell with the assistance of some sixth year boys who happened to be passing.

146

Worse was to come at lunchtime: a group of severely maladjusted twelve-year olds spent a large proportion of their lunch break in wrecking, and subsequently flooding, the junior boys' toilets. Fortunately, I collared the obvious ringleader – a fat little boy with thin greasy hair and an intellect to match – and frogmarched him along to the headmaster's room.

'Right, sonny,' I cautioned before sending him into Mr Ross. 'Take that chewing gum out of your mouth, stop playing with that ridiculous yo-yo and stand to attention. You're in secondary school now – and you're already in serious trouble.'

'Aye, aye. Shoor thing,' he drawled, completely unconcerned and oblivious to all of my instructions.

I couldn't believe such dumb insolence, especially from a pupil who had still to join the school. 'Listen, son,' I explained severely. 'You've started off badly. Very badly. A lot of people here will be looking out for you once you start with us in August. What's your name, anyway?' I demanded sharply.

'McShane. Toammy McShane, if it's anythin' tae yoo.'

'Don't be so –' I stopped in mid-sentence: 'What did you say your name was?'

'McShane. Toammy McShane. Ur ye deef?'

'You're not . . . by any chance . . . you're not related to . . . you're not – are you?'

I was unable to frame the question properly, perhaps because in my heart of hearts I already knew the answer. The family resemblance was only too apparent.

'Rosie McShane?' he confirmed my worst fears. 'Aye. Ah'm hur wee brerr. She told me this place wis a rerr laff, an' she's spoat-oan.'

Awash with distress, I thrust him unceremoniusly into the headmaster's study and hurried away to the staffroom. Rose McShane's brother – and for the next four years. Possibly five? Or even six? It doesn't bear thinking about.

I wonder if it's too late to apply for a transfer?

Postscript

As this, his second volume of educational memoirs, draws to an uncertain conclusion, it can be safely revealed that Morris Simpson did *not* apply for a transfer during the summer months.

There would have been no point. Wherever he could have gone, there would have been a Rose McShane. Or her brother. Or both.

No matter the school, no matter the area, teachers all over the country will testify to the fact that every class does, indeed, 'have one': the pupil who has scant respect for authority, the pupil who is ever eager to draw attention to him or herself, and who is ever alert to any conceivable opportunity to disrupt a carefully prepared lesson plan. The presence of these pupils is, of course, one of the factors which make teaching a job of such infinite variety, if not pleasure.

Morris, in his third and fourth years of teaching, had discovered many more such diverse aspects of teaching, as these recollections have revealed. It had been a period of increasing demands and increasing change within Scottish education, but Morris still seemed to like the job, in a perverse sort of way.

His diaries continued to appear in the *Times Scottish Education Supplement*, where his traumatic experiences with Tommy McShane soon made him wonder, like every teacher, why he bothered joining the profession in the first place. At least, as the sole staff nominee for a place on Parkland's school board, he felt there would now be a chance to forge a new path for education, a chance to enter into a dynamic new partnership with the parents of those children entrusted to his care.

It is all another sorry story. In his eventual experiences with the school board at Parkland High, Morris Simpson soon discovered that the practice failed to live up to the theory.

In education, it was ever thus.

Acknowledgements

Many thanks to all the teachers and schools who have contributed to this book, whether they know it or not.

Special thanks once again to Mr Tact of Drumclog, Jim Dunbar, who contributed more than most (in exchange for the occasional meal), to Christine, Linda and Margaret, who also gave the occasional story (and particularly Linda for the title), and to my mother and father (who didn't get a mention last time round – sorry, mum!)

Thanks also to Willis Pickard, WEEF, and all at TSES, also to all at Hodder & Stoughton, At Hodder, particular thanks to Brian Steven and Michael Soper, and to everyone else who had anything to do with preparing, publishing, and (especially!) selling it.

Finally, thanks to the three women in my life – Judith, Kathryn and Alyson – for lots of love and laughter. It's all dedicated to them.